Men, Machines and
Sacred Cows

ALSO BY HRH THE DUKE OF EDINBURGH

Men, Machines and Sacred Cows

HRH THE DUKE OF EDINBURGH

HAMISH HAMILTON

LONDON

First published in Great Britain 1984
by Hamish Hamilton Ltd
Garden House, 57–59 Long Acre, London WC2E 9JZ

Permission has kindly been given by Routledge & Kegan Paul Ltd for the author to
quote a passage from *Archetype* by Anthony Stevens.

British Library Cataloguing in Publication Data

Philip, *Prince, consort of Elizabeth II, Queen of*
    Great Britain
    Men, machines and sacred cows.
    I. Title
    082

    ISBN 0-241-11174-9

Typeset by Rowland Phototypesetting Ltd
Printed in Great Britain by
St Edmundsbury Press, Bury St Edmunds, Suffolk

Contents

Contents

Introduction

Regular readers of the Court Circular will know how often such words as 'opened', 'unveiled', 'inaugurated', 'attended' and 'addressed' appear in that column. The words look innocent enough, but in almost every case they conceal the fact that a few, and in some instances quite a lot of, words had to be said as well. In my case this entails much head-scratching and pencil-chewing before I manage, more or less successfully, to compose something vaguely appropriate to the occasion. But while speeches, addresses and lectures account for a high proportion of chewed pencils, the composition of written messages, forewords and articles accounts for several more.

Professional writers and speakers obviously have their problems, but at least they are free to choose their subjects. If I accept an invitation to speak or to write a message, the subject is chosen for me and, to make matters worse, the people I am expected to address know much more about the subject than I do. I imagine barristers have something of the same problem when preparing a case involving special or technical issues.

Some invitations suggest a light-hearted approach but trying to be funny is a great deal more difficult than trying to be serious. In any case, what may strike me as a witty comment can easily turn out to be painfully tactless to a specialist audience. Wit is subjective, and there is nothing more disconcerting than a confident shaft of wit failing dismally to strike home. Trying to explain the point only makes matters worse. Well, perhaps there is something more disconcerting, and that is when an audience laughs uproariously at a line spoken in all seriousness. In that sense, writing is a great deal safer.

I have now been struggling with these problems for some thirty years so that the collection of short messages to conferences and programmes and of forewords to books alone fills quite a large section of a filing cabinet. When the idea for this book was first put forward I was appalled by the amount of shelf space taken up by speeches, addresses, lectures and articles.

All this was the raw material and this book is the result of the Editor browsing through this accumulation of words. Part of the deal was that the choice, editing and arrangement of the pieces would be entirely in his hands, and the reason is simply that I am a very bad judge of my own work. Pieces that may have given me particular satisfaction at the time, for one reason or another, may well not be read with the same enthusiasm by someone else. On the other hand, there have been a few occasions when bits have been received with rather more interest than I expected. More important perhaps is that most of the material was either written or delivered for a particular audience on a particular occasion and usually in rather special circumstances. When an essay or a speech is read several years later by someone not directly involved with the original occasion, and as one of a number of essays on similar or related subjects, the impression is bound to be different.

The difference between a free society and one in which all issues are governed by inflexible dogma is the constant exchange of ideas. This book is just another contribution to that exchange in the hope that it may start trains of thought in other minds and help readers to see some of the problems of this life perhaps from a different point of view.

PART I

Men, Computers and Sacred Cows

ONE

'People are People'

YEARS AGO I was invited to address a group of students in Cardiff and, being a young, bright-eyed and bushy-tailed Chancellor of the University of Wales, I accepted. The gist of my remarks was that students had qualified to attend university and so I assumed that they had a superior intelligence to their less fortunate contemporaries'. I said I thought they were very important because what this country needed above all was brains. This remark went down rather better than expected, in fact it started a minor riot. It was only after it had subsided and I had managed to finish my few words of wisdom, that I discovered that the brewery company in Cardiff was called Braines.

Chancellors are, of course, more decorative than functional but, in my experience they do have one quite useful function. The heat and burden of running most universities falls on the Vice-Chancellors. Strong, stalwart and determined characters all, but it is rather lonely at the top, and Chancellors can provide a sympathetic ear for all their pent-up troubles and frustrations.

It may come as a bit of a shock to realise that such lofty figures as Vice-Chancellors are even remotely human. Indeed I find it takes a positive act of will to realise that such almost mythical officials as the Chairman of I.C.I., the Secretary of the T.U.C., the Archbishop of Wales, or any member of the Cabinet for that matter, are just people, struggling with special responsibilities perhaps, but people like everyone else. Oddly enough, it seems to be just as difficult for people in authority to remember that everybody else are people too.

The fact is that people are people and not things; neither are they numbers nor percentages nor society, nor the community, nor even a mass. People – individual people – are unique. The only thing we have in common is our human nature and even that varies as much as our fingerprints. Perhaps most important of all and apparently most easily forgotten is that the whole bag of tricks of political theories, economic and educational systems, social structures and the rest are all for the sake of people and not, as one might suspect, the other way round.

The same can be said about Universities, Polytechnics and Technical Colleges. They are not there to meet the needs of Government or industry or the professions. I find it very irritating when I see criticisms of Universities for not turning out enough engineers for industry. Strange as it may seem, I believe that students should be included as people and allowed to make their own decisions. The real purpose of these institutions is to help people develop their talents so as to give them the opportunity to choose what service they can best offer their fellow-citizens and which will allow them to make a reasonable living at the same time.

Judging by the amount of time and space given to such things as the national economy, the balance of payments, the size of the G.N.P., the Public Sector Borrowing Requirement and the figures of unemployment, you would think that they were all more important than people. This obsession with things can be taken to absurd lengths. When prices started to go up after the French Revolution, Marat is supposed to have told the Chamber of Deputies that the solution was simply to 'shoot the shopkeepers'. Marx had much the same idea, only he wanted to shoot the middle-class for exploiting the workers.

These things are not more important than people, and furthermore I do not believe that individuals find it at all easy to relate to these abstract concepts so beloved by politicians and economists. How can anyone see his work in relation to the balance of payments or the national economy, or the idea that industry creates wealth? The primary concern of the individual is for his own balance of payments problem and his own personal domestic economy and his own wealth. It is easy enough to accept the need for taxation, in principle; it is not always so easy for the individual to see why he has to pay so much or why it has to be such a complicated business. As to the national figures for unemployment, an individual is either employed or unemployed, the national totals are not directly relevant to him.

Even a computer takes time to work out the macro-statistics of the national economy, so that when they are ready to be published the conditions which created the statistics are long since past. People living in the real world are constantly dealing with the present conditions and future possibilities; they are reacting to a new situation long before the statistics can reveal how they dealt with the old one. For those who wanted to see, it was quite apparent that small businesses were in a state of decline six or seven years ago, but it is only recently that the statistics are beginning to show the extent of the decline.

Anyway, it is not the national economy which decides the circumstances of the individual, it is the other way round. Governments can control such things as the rate of public spending, the rate of taxation and hence the rate of inflation. They can lay down the rules governing industrial, commercial and professional enterprise, but the state of the economy is decided by the way people respond to these conditions. The Government cannot order rates of enterprise, creativity, productivity or profitability; these are decided by people.

It has always been easy to find fault with others when things go wrong but it is worth remembering that we are all subject to the same human fears and emotions, ambitions and prejudices. Different occupations may have different interests but they don't change human nature. The leader who wants to do well for his Union is driven by much the same motives as the manager who wants to do well for his Company. The desire for a bigger pay packet is the same as the desire for a higher salary or a bigger income. Bad industrial relations cut both ways. A work force can be demoralised by bad management and management can be demoralised just as easily by unreasonable militancy. People go on being people whatever their occupation and the factors which govern their relationships are crucial to their ability to cooperate.

The pernicious influence of industrial conflict goes much further. It hampers efficiency, it lowers productivity, it blunts the competitive edge. All this leads to a fall in confidence and to the natural reluctance of those who save or those who manage the savings of others to provide the necessary funds for investment in new plant and machinery.

It is only natural that people in all situations should have a primary concern for their own welfare. What is easily forgotten is that every enterprise and every occupation has become increasingly interdependent. Every section of the economy is influenced by every success and also by every failure in our system. Like the parts of a watch, it only needs one faulty component to slow down the whole mechanism. No amount of winding or banging will make it go properly until the fault is repaired.

The Christian, or any other church for that matter, is not some disembodied entity with a few self-appointed spokesmen. Churches are made up of people and, whatever the official doctrine may be on paper, the practical test is the extent to which the people who claim to be members live out the doctrine in their daily lives; and the doctrine should be judged by those who succeed and not by those who fail to live up to it. Similarly, universities can provide facilities but the will to learn has got to come from the people who are supposed to do the studying.

We have also discovered that there is no absolute statistical relationship between the amount of money spent on scientific research, the output of useful discovery and profitable industrial innovation. Only people with ambition, talent and enterprise can bridge the gaps and transform one into the other, and then, as a rule, only if they can see some positive advantage in the effort.

The system of mass oppression which passes for enlightened government in so many countries of the world is not invariably the result of a deliberate intention to oppress, but rather the unintentional consequence of people acting with the best possible motives and, in most cases, in the bland assumption that a democratic process can decide what is right and what is wrong. In fact, all it decides is what the majority has been persuaded it wants to do. Furthermore, a Parliamentary democracy will only work in its proper sense if people want it to work that way. If people become careless in their attitude to democracy and political morality, it is only too easily reduced to a cynical system of Government by statistics and head-counting.

An Indian sage has written: 'Socio-political ideologies uninspired by high moral and spiritual values tend to nourish the lower self of man from which proceed selfishness and intolerance, violence and war.' Yet, of one thing I am fairly sure: I do not believe that the basic factors and characteristics of human nature have changed very much, if at all. It is just that the conditions under which people are required to operate have been drastically changed.

Quite apart from the changes to the physical environment and material standards, there has been a dramatic change in the intellectual environment. By that I mean the immense increase in knowledge of the facts of our planet and universe. We have gained in knowledge of the outside, of external nature, at the expense of our knowledge of the inside, of our own hearts and minds.

Within 150 years we have progressed from horse-drawn and wind-blown transport to machines which can fly passengers at twice the speed of sound. But people go on in much the same way. The only difference between highwaymen and hijackers and terrorists is that the latter use politics as a justification.

I suspect that it is this greater knowledge of things, and particularly the success of organised industry, which has encouraged the belief that human communities can be organised and controlled like some huge piece of machinery. It seems that it is just a question of getting the systems right and we shall achieve the perfect civilisation. In practice, of course, cultures and civilisations only develop through voluntary co-operation between people inspired by high moral and spiritual values. The standards of morality and behaviour demanded by such civilisations may have clashed with some of mankind's baser instincts but the mechanisation of society looks like achieving a direct confrontation with human nature as a whole. Perhaps it is not altogether surprising that so many individuals are confused and unhappy.

The arguments for the mechanised society are compelling and they are advanced with the best possible intentions, but I am beginning to suspect that they miss, or perhaps they just forget, the whole point of human life. A life devoid of challenge or risk, an existence of total stability and total security, may be splendid for cabbages but it would not be much fun for people.

I do not believe there can be real satisfaction of any kind unless the individual can come to see a purpose in his own individual existence, not just as a slave of the national interest, and recognises that the only thing which can make life tolerable for his fellow beings, as well as those who will come after him, is the responsibility he takes for his own attitudes and his own actions. It is not what people are forced to do by law, it is what they want to do by conviction that decides the state of civilisation in which they are going to live.

Shakespeare has Cassius say: 'The fault, dear Brutus, is not in our stars, But in ourselves.' There is nothing wrong with this world which cannot be cured by people. Almost nothing in this world will be put right by theories, systems and organisations or by socio-political ideologies just by themselves.

Equally, there is nothing wrong with such things as material prosperity, or commercial enterprise, or academic scholarship, or scientific knowledge, or artistic accomplishment, or even meditation; but none of these is really crucial to the human condition. They may provide the means to an end, but they are not ends in themselves.

They could just as easily be part of what Frankl calls the 'existential vacuum' unless they provide the people – that is the individual workers, managers, academics, scientists and artists – with a personal reason for their existence and with an understanding for the need of certain standards of morality and behaviour. After 20,000 years of human existence there really cannot be much doubt about which attitudes and behaviour make for a civilised society; but every individual has got to discover the need for them in his own way.

Once an individual has established the meaning and purpose of his particular unique existence and understands the value of his personal contribution to the totality of human existence, the distinction between good and bad becomes a great deal clearer. But the choice between them has still to be made and the decisions which follow from that choice have to be made all the time. It is these daily, even hourly, decisions which gradually establish the worth and humanity of each individual. It is not what a man does for a living, it is how he lives his life that is important. There is no difference between a crooked lawyer and a dishonest social worker. A thief is a thief whether he is a professor or an under-graduate.

One of the consequences of our complex modern way of life which makes things so difficult for individuals is the apparent necessity for people to be surveyed, recorded, numbered, pigeon-holed, and above all put into categories. Everybody has to be divided up into classes and occupations, workers and managers, income, ethnic and age groups, and any number of others, including of course the 'don't knows' who figure so largely in opinion polls. Yet for human purposes they are all totally irrelevant. If you come to think of it, there are really only two categories of people, the good and the bad or the decent and the indecent.

The only trouble is that people are not consistent members of either category. It is only too easy to slip from one to the other in a matter of minutes. It can happen between one decision and one action and the next, or it can happen between one part of a lifetime and the next. Equally unsatisfactory, for those who glory in their prejudices, is that the two categories are found at every level of society and in every other category of people you care to put together.

Contrary to evident opinion in some quarters, there is absolutely no evidence to suggest that any one group of people has all the virtues or that any other group has all the vices. Even in the concentration camps there were kindly guards and brutal prisoners. And, just in case we all get too smug, decency has nothing to do with intelligence. In fact, it is much easier for the intelligent to go wrong because they find it so simple to justify in their own eyes whatever it is that they feel like doing. Frederick the Great is supposed to have said: 'I take what I want, I can always find pedants to prove my rights!' What is more, the intelligent are capable of leading others astray as well, since so many of them seem to suffer from the 'governess' or 'I know best' syndrome.

What is quite certain is that those who can see no point or purpose in their lives, and cannot comprehend their unique freedom to choose their attitudes, are far more likely to fall into the indecent category, and fall into it more frequently.

They may not be intentionally or chronically bad or vicious but, if they have nothing to guide them and cannot discriminate between right and wrong, they are only too likely to fall into the trap of believing that pleasure and happiness are the only ultimate ambition and that these can be achieved by self-indulgence. With no other thought in mind than pleasure and happiness they are living in that 'existential vacuum' which leads only to boredom, frustration and violence or to an obsession with sex and pornography.

On the other hand, those whose work or creative talents, or religious conviction, or suffering, or love, have given them a vision of what they are capable of contributing to human existence, are more likely to be found in the decent category. I say 'more likely' because it is easy to go to extremes, and a fanatical attachment to an idea often leads to the conviction that any means are justified by such a glorious end. In practice, of course, the better the end the more decent the means ought to be for achieving it. Or, to put it the other way round, if the means are violent the end will be the same.

There is no single or exclusive way to the discovery of purpose and meaning and all that follows from it. What makes each of us unique is that the discovery and the choices and decisions we make are ours alone, they have nothing to do with political or economic systems, material conditions, environment, genetics or the retail price index. Oppression can silence a man but he is still free to choose his attitude.

It seems to me, therefore, that everything begins with the individual and it is people who decide what sort of communities they are going to live in. Whether it is a Kibbutz, a Hutterite community, a commune, a village or a city, it is the people who are going to decide whether it will be humanly tolerable and civilised or whether it will degenerate into a human jungle. Furthermore, the decision still remains with the inhabitants, unless they manage to escape from an unsatisfactory community, in spite of cumbersome structures of Government and administration which well-meaning people have devised for them.

Tidy and rational mechanical systems will always appeal to some people and they may well succeed in imposing them on some communities from time to time, but in the long run they are certain to founder on the rock of human nature with its even balance of strength and weakness and its potential for good and evil. Higher standards of civilisation will only be achieved by building on its strength and by encouraging its potential for good.

It seems to me therefore that we all need to be reminded that our first responsibility is to be concerned about our own behaviour, our own relationships with other people and our own attitudes to what is right and wrong. There can be no such thing as a compassionate and caring society if the individuals are not compassionate and caring.

Polonius says this to Laertes: 'This above all, to thine own self be true, and it must follow as the night the day – thou canst not then be false to any man.' We may be frantic to go out and correct all the apparent injustices and skulduggery of this materialist world but it is worth remembering that they are not to do with one system or another, they are to do with the weaknesses of human nature.

The clue to the reform of society is the development of individuals into decent and responsible citizens, each trusting the other to do his best with whatever talents and opportunities he may have. This is not something which can be imposed on people. I think it can only be done by the people who have discovered a purpose in their lives and who see the virtue of decency and are willing to help others by example to go out and make these discoveries for themselves.

TWO

Leisure

I HAVE no doubt at all that everyone knows what I mean by leisure but, to make quite certain, I want to quote a definition by an American, Doctor Paul Weiss. He says that 'Leisure time is that portion of the day not used for meeting the exigencies of existence'. This means that in that time it is possible to do things for their own sake and not as a means to an end. Just in case there is still a shadow of doubt let me quote the Oxford English Dictionary: 'Leisure; the state of having time at one's disposal; time which one can expend as one pleases; free or unoccupied time.'

Leisure is certainly not a manifestation of modern civilisation. In the strictly hierarchical and the slave-based societies the subject of leisure loomed very large for a proportion of the population. (It was of course no problem to the rest of the population because they didn't have any.) Aristotle for instance suggested that the purpose of education was the wise use of leisure. I suspect that some students, and not necessarily of philosophy, are more likely to say that education provides almost un-limited leisure.

There is evidence that primitive man was also confronted by leisure. It is reasonable to suppose that cave-paintings, and indeed all art forms down the ages, had their origin in leisure time, because I do not suppose that these ancient artists could be described as professionals in the sense that they practised their art as one of the exigencies of their existence.

In the 1880 American Presidential campaign, James A. Garfield put his finger on it when he suggested that the struggle of the human race is divided into two chapters: 'First, the fight to get leisure; and then the second fight of civilisation – what shall we do with our leisure when we get it?'

Although the definition of leisure applies today just as much as ever, the problems which leisure raises now are of an entirely different order. The mechanical or technological age in which we live has produced a totally new form of civilisation. For one thing a much greater proportion of the population of technologically advanced countries has more leisure time at its disposal. Then there are more and different ways of using leisure time, while increasing prosperity is giving people wider opportunities to fill their leisure time with rewarding activities.

Leisure, in fact, which for most people throughout history was only on the fringe of existence, is now rapidly becoming a central feature of our whole egalitarian environment. Garfield's first fight is being won – at any rate in the more advanced countries.

I must confess that I am interested in leisure in the same way that a poor man is interested in money. I can't get enough of it. Furthermore, I have no problem whatever in filling my leisure time and I worry not at all whether what I do is good or wise or likely to improve my character or to help me become a 'whole man'.

I mention all this because great and worthy thinkers down the ages have succeeded in creating out of the simple facts of work and leisure a veritable cockpit of moral, philosophical and even religious argument. I am not going to concern myself with this philosophical debate because it inevitably leads into the ridiculous discussion of what is the proper use of leisure. Quite enough human misery is caused by the self-righteous trying to impose their myopic standards on the rest of the community. Leisure is a fact and what you do with it is a matter of individual choice influenced no doubt by personal, ethical, moral or religious factors as the case may be; and, of course, by the knowledge or lack of knowledge of the possibilities.

If you accept Aristotle's view of education and leisure you may have difficulty in finding a job, but then that was not his problem. If you subscribe to what is sometimes called 'the Protestant Ethic', that only honest hard work is good, you will then always and inevitably have a bad conscience about having any leisure at all and a sense of guilt whatever you do with it. I am sure it is this Puritanical hangover which produces the attitude that the only things which are fun are either immoral, illegal or fattening.

Morality after all is a matter of conscience and, as Julian Huxley put it, 'conscience is not something given ready-made whether by heredity or divine implantation'. Western morality is the outcome of mainly Christian beliefs and the accumulated experience of mankind. A lot of this morality has been incorporated in the law so that most things considered to be immoral are now illegal. There are exceptions of course, such as war morality and sexual morality which seem to get bent without much difficulty to suit the occasion.

However this is not a treatise on morality and the point I am trying to make is that modern civilisation in practice is creating a new ethic, which is simply that work is a means of gaining leisure. Unfortunately it is creating it in a typically human, haphazard and confused way. I think we are all agreed that without moral complications the ideal is to do as little work as possible for the highest possible reward. But is everyone agreed that we should work shorter hours each day, or fewer days each week or fewer weeks each year? Dr Marion Clawson, for instance, has worked out that if you reduce the average number of hours worked in the week from forty to thirty-two a company can either cut each day's work from eight to six and a half hours, or reduce the number of working days in the week from five to four or, as a third alternative, give one week's paid vacation in three quarters of the year with a month's vacation in the fourth quarter and six months every five years, or of course any combination or permutation of these alternatives. Whatever you choose, the effect is to increase the total time available for leisure.

Very reasonably, the immediate preoccupation is to reduce working hours but it seems to me, at least, that we should be equally concerned that this extra leisure time should come in the most convenient and acceptable form. Otherwise people are likely suddenly to find that they have been forced to give up working time; after all, quite a lot of people like working, and have failed to get the sort of leisure time they can best use.

This argument is in very general terms because the division of work and leisure is not always sharp and distinct. Some may use free time from one job to take another in order to make more money. Some are so involved in their jobs that they do not make any distinction at all. Others can manage to integrate work and leisure activities in such a way that there is no formal allocation of time to one or the other. Just think how much business is transacted in sports clubs, on fishing expeditions or even in restaurants and night clubs. (I am not of course referring to every transaction conducted in the latter places.) Other people are even prepared to work long hours for relatively little money because they feel their work has some special quality about it, in the social services sense, for instance, or because it gives them particular satisfaction. The selection of a job is seldom entirely dependent upon the pay and prospects. Fringe benefits of all kinds play a large part, not least the opportunities for leisure occupations.

Leisure is only a problem in two senses. When any particular activity becomes popular with a great many people there is inevitably a difficulty in finding suitable space and facilities to cater for the demand. This problem is naturally far more serious in the small overcrowded British Islands than for instance in the U.S.A. For example, Britain is rapidly running out of suitable coast line for all the people who want to take their holidays by the sea. The hills and wild country can hardly contain the new army of campers and hill-climbers, stretches of inland water attract sailing boats, water skiers, swimmers and skin-divers, fishermen, naturalists, bird-watchers and hunters. The ski-ing resorts of Europe are getting more crowded every year and any specially attractive summer resort area is developed so rapidly and ruthlessly that its character is bound to be changed by the sheer weight of numbers of people pouring into it.

This problem, then, is already acute and will become a great deal worse in the future. The difficulty is to know how to cope with it. Some people are already calling for direct Government involvement. They argue that Government virtually controls every other sphere of activity of its citizens, so it might as well control the provisions for leisure time as well. Only a co-ordinated plan backed by legislation can possibly prevent a state of complete chaos developing in a very short time.

At the other end there are those who object on principle to Government interference in anything and see in leisure the last remaining freedom for the individual.

I do not pretend to know what is the right answer, but provision for leisure is already very big business and I cannot help feeling that unrestricted exploitation is not necessarily going to achieve the sort of long-term pattern we would like to see. Furthermore, if the whole development of leisure facilities is to be decided entirely by what is profitable, many opportunities will be missed. If profit is the criterion you may get a lot of golf courses but you're unlikely to get mountain shelters for climbers or properly established camping sites. You'll get motels and car parks but no nature reserves or national parks.

The other sense in which leisure is a problem is in the selection of what to do with it. People must be in a position to choose leisure activities which are going to give them pleasure or satisfaction. I do not think anyone likes being bored; boredom is merely a symptom of not knowing what to do with leisure, and ignorance is a great begetter of pride. It is quite ridiculous to get angry or indignant with people who do not know what to do in their spare time. In most cases they are totally ignorant of the possibilities. People are inclined to make bland statements about the duty of individuals to develop their talents to the full. This is all very laudable, but say that to an adolescent and you might as well tell a blind man to see red.

In many cases there is virtually no provision for anything more rewarding than paying to watch other people playing games. We sometimes seem to forget that sports were intended for the pleasure of those taking part and not only for the entertainment of spectators. For this, our traditional views on education and work must take a lot of the blame. The attitude is that there must be nothing frivolous in education, and hard work is the only way to a good life. To this should be added, I think, the modification of those influences which create the conscience, that sense of right and wrong which is the effective controller of behaviour. By that I mean the increasing isolation of individual families, the increasing materialism in ordinary education and the increasing divergence of science and religion. These have all made it more difficult for young people to find a convincing set of rules for living. Result: boredom, frustration, anti-social or more usually anti-authority behaviour, delinquency and the excitement of crime.

After all, it is not people who are good and bad, it is what they do.

If a community believes that it is unnecessary and a waste of time to expose the younger generation to the worthwhile things of this life, it cannot in fairness complain when that generation finds its own ways of filling its leisure hours. The problem is that there has been a fundamental change in the practice of living which has not been matched by a change in the theory.

In Thomas Jefferson's time 94 per cent of all Americans lived on farmsteads with all that implies as a way of life. In 1960 an average of over 60 per cent of Americans lived in towns and cities. By the year 2000 this will have increased to over 70 per cent of a population of 350 million. These statistics imply a totally different type of existence and demand a totally different approach to the problems of life. A bad social organisation is as unhealthy for a community as a bad digestion is unpleasant for the body.

It apparently never occurred to that self-righteous fellow (or perhaps it was a woman) when he invented the saying that 'the Devil finds work for idle hands' that he was passing the buck. Idleness was immoral and corrupt so it is not surprising that no one felt it necessary to relieve the Devil of this particular responsibility except by recommending more work.

The worst feature about idleness is that it leads to boredom which is one of the most deadly afflictions that anyone can suffer. De Chardin, in his book *The Future of Man*, goes even further. 'Mankind is bored,' he asserts. 'Perhaps this is the underlying cause of all our troubles. We no longer know what to do with ourselves. Hence in social terms the disorderly turmoil of individuals pursuing conflicting and egoistical aims; and on the national scale, the chaos of armed conflict in which, for want of a better object, the excess of accumulated energy is destructively released. Idleness, mother of all vices.'

Now that so much work is dull and limited in time, the Devil is kept pretty busy. But surely it should be possible for idle hands to be tough without being vicious; to live dangerously without being destructive; to be enterprising without being criminal. If this is possible, and I am convinced that it is, then it is necessary to create the facilities and to let people become aware of them.

Today's ideal human being appears to be what is sometimes termed a well-adjusted personality, or what H. G. Wells described as a 'jelly-bellied lotus-eater'. It is rather like suggesting that the only well-adjusted chickens in a factory farm are those who make no attempt to escape. No intelligent human being has ever been satisfied with his general environment. Dissatisfaction and frustration have been the hallmark of all great reformers and innovators.

By all means let us be thankful that there are so many people who are content to be bored, or who are scared to be unconventional, or who are simply satisfied with their lot. These people fortunately create no problems. It is the ones with initiative and courage and a sense of dissatisfaction who are so easily perverted unless their gifts are attracted into constructive activities.

If they want a tough physical challenge let them try mountain climbing, where the fascination is not in risking death by ignorance or incompetence but in successfully overcoming the risks by careful training and preparation. If they want speed, then let them have it under conditions where the thrill is just as great but where the general public is not involved.

It was hailed as a brilliant discovery that no two people share the same fingerprints. It should be an even more obvious discovery that no two people have the same personality. Vast numbers of people can be induced by convention to conform to a stereotyped existence but somewhere, somehow, the individual personality will assert itself. Without the opportunity and the freedom to choose interesting, rewarding, satisfying or fascinating things to do, the individual can only assert himself by rebelling against the restraints of society.

I have no sympathy with people who claim to know what is good for others. My contention is that no one should be prevented from taking part in any reasonable activity through ignorance or lack of facilities and no one should be forced into crime because it is the conventional thing to do.

The difficulty about introducing children, or adults for that matter, to possible leisure time activities is that it is such an intensely personal matter. An improving and uplifting experience for one is a dead loss for another. It is no good trying to encourage an appreciation of music in someone who is tone-deaf. By some means or other people, and particularly young people, must be exposed to as wide a range of worthwhile activities as possible so as to allow them to become aware of the opportunities open to them. It is important to start young because up to a certain age people do not mind being taught; after a certain age people hate being beginners. On the other hand the process must continue past childhood because adult tastes are frequently different from those of children, and an ability to play games, however healthy, is not really enough.

I do not want to give the impression that the only use of leisure is self-indulgent amusement. All voluntary work of any sort is a leisure activity and for many it is the most rewarding and interesting use of their discretionary time. Young people in particular are enormously attracted by the invitation to help others, especially if it demands some form of qualification such as first aid training or learning to communicate with the deaf. The response to opportunities for voluntary service overseas demonstrates only too clearly that there is enormous scope among young people for this use of leisure.

I suspect sometimes that people are put off attempting things which they would really very much like to do for fear of doing them badly or because they feel it is undignified to be a beginner. In the sense of professional work, if a job is worth doing it is worth doing well, but as far as leisure is concerned Oscar Wilde had the right idea when he said, 'If a thing is worth doing, it's worth doing badly.'

The range of choice is of course immense but it is this feature which makes leisure so vitally important. In this age of mass-employment, rationalised food, identical housing, in fact a total daily environment which is common in all essentials to the vast majority of the population, the only possible point for any individuality to break through is during leisure time. It is the only discretionary time left, it is the only moment when we can snap our fingers at the rest of humanity and do something wholly satisfying to ourselves either alone or with like-minded friends. It is the last refuge of individuality.

Having said that, I must immediately qualify it with an apparent contradiction. Owing to the immense increase in world population, which means an increasing density of people, and owing to the steadily increasing complexity of man's environment, it is inevitable that there must be a complementary increase in the restriction and control of human existence, both individually and internationally. The tendency to powerful centralised Government, the discussion of the idea of world Government, and the already extensive international control of monetary arrangements are obvious examples of this tendency. Orderly peaceful existence depends upon discipline and restraint.

This apparently contradicts the idea of the independence of the individual. But this process of centralisation and restriction can in fact give the individual the opportunity for greater freedom for his conscience and for the things that affect him personally, such as his leisure, his beliefs and his artistic expression, provided always that he has the will and the ability to use that extra freedom.

Once it is accepted that the time we have for leisure has its own value and importance in the modern pattern of civilisation several things follow. For instance it means that the work people do for a living need not be the central feature of their existence. The moment work becomes a means to an end and not an end in itself it removes the status value of any particular job, because it may well be that the leisure activity confers a higher status than the job. Therefore leisure occupations may well have a considerable influence on the whole structure of society.

Relationships at work are conditioned by strict systems of seniority, pay scales, grades of responsibility. In the community, relationships are conditioned by the size and location of the home, the number of cars owned and so on. Leisure occupations cut across status at work or status in the community. A common interest in skiing for instance, or sailing, washes out all other differences. Young or old, highly paid or relatively poor, manager or truck driver, all establish a new relationship within the leisure occupation which they share.

Taking the intrinsic value of leisure a bit further it also suggests the possibility of following a course of education and training solely for a leisure occupation while making a living at any convenient job which needs to be done. As a matter of fact many artists do something like this already. They may not be able to live on their painting, so they take some other job, teaching perhaps, to enable them to go on painting.

It means that many of the jobs which have been abandoned because they were considered unsuitable or beneath the dignity of an educated person may be taken up again by people who are more concerned with what they do with their leisure than how they make a living.

It means that it does not matter so much if you wind up with a dead end job because opportunities in leisure activities are virtually unlimited.

In fact I think it would be true to say that for the first time in history ordinary men and women are being released from the bondage of perpetual work. For the first time in history men and women are finding that they have time to choose something they really like doing. The problem is to make certain that more people become aware of the opportunities so that they are able to make a choice, and also to ensure that the facilities are fully and properly provided.

It needs more than a generous encouragement of the traditional arts and music or an amused tolerance towards the apparently less intellectual pursuits. It needs to stimulate a social conscience about leisure in the same way that the social conscience of the nineteenth century had to be stirred about poverty. Boredom and idleness are poverty of the spirit. It will need enlightened leaders to show the way to a fuller civilisation based on the rewarding use of leisure. These leaders are in the universities today and their opportunities are immense.

It is all too easy to talk about the free world and the freedom of the individual but in practice it is leisure and the ability to choose what to do with it which really makes a man a free and civilised individual.

THREE

Propaganda

I THINK it might be as well to explain what I mean by propaganda. I would define it as the deliberate manipulation of information presented to a selected public in order to create a particular impression in the public mind. I do not mean that it necessarily excludes the truth, far from it. The most effective propaganda is that which is nearest the truth, provided, of course, that it is in your interest to present something near the truth and provided it is presented in such a way that people are prepared to believe it. However, you will be aware that there is strong evidence from political circles that whopping lies repeated often enough are eventually accepted not just as the truth but as dogma.

Propaganda is important today because the armed forces of the major powers have virtually put themselves out of business as a means of settling international disputes. They have become much too efficient in their ability to destroy and, as constituted at present, they have no other means by which they can put into effect the wishes of the political Government.

Rightly or wrongly, propaganda has not been considered as one of the military arts.

At any previous time in history arguments between nations – even relatively small ones – were settled by force, without directly involving more than a small proportion of the populations, without doing too much material damage, except in religious or civil wars when things always get out of hand. Today, everybody knows the completely disastrous consequences of an all-out armed conflict particularly if it were to involve any nuclear powers. It is true that, as a consequence, non-nuclear powers can indulge in conventional warfare with less fear of intervention by the nuclear powers, but then the number of nuclear powers seems to be on the increase, and the destructiveness of conventional weapons is greater than ever. This means that any fear or reluctance to use the available military force gives the art of propaganda a significance in international relations which up till now has been reserved solely for military power. Gunboat diplomacy is a thing of the past – propaganda diplomacy is the new thing.

Propaganda is important for another reason. It is already the most powerful weapon in the hands of subversive and revolutionary elements, be they native or foreign. It should be perfectly clear by now that you cannot fight subversive propaganda with conventional military or police action. Just as there is no single weapon which is effective in every kind of combat, so it is essential to find the most suitable weapon to counter an attack by an opponent. Strangely enough, it nearly always ends up with like fighting like. Propaganda can only be countered by propaganda.

The means by which propaganda reaches its intended target obviously includes all the conventional mass media, but there are other ways. Spreading rumours and gossip; posters; leaflets; pamphlets; tapes; public speeches; questions at press conferences; while international conferences, cultural, technical, political and scientific events of all kinds, can be put to good use by an efficient propaganda machine. A little imagination can suggest many other possibilities.

Propaganda has, of course, played a great part during active hostilities ever since Man came down from the trees – and perhaps even before. What is a display of aggression if not a piece of propaganda? In the old days propaganda was used for two purposes – to encourage and boost the morale of friends and to discourage and demoralise the enemy. War dances were good for morale, and all sorts of fantastic clothing, or none at all, were used to strike fear into the enemy. History books are full of brave speeches of the 'Once more into the breach . . .' variety, uttered by gallant leaders to rouse the spirits of the less belligerent. Fearful tales of the wickedness of the enemy quickly became folklore. In the early nineteenth century countless English mothers tried to intimidate their children by suggesting that 'Old Boney will get you' if they did not behave.

It is quite extraordinary what men will do when they are convinced of the righteousness of their cause. During the Crusades each side was equally determined that death in battle meant a certain place in paradise – I imagine a different paradise for each side. Even in wars between Christian countries, whether the cause was religious or not, both claimed God was on their side. You have only to listen to the propaganda broadcasts or watch the television programmes from Ireland or the Comrade countries to find the same kind of one-sided obsession.

Atrocity stories are no modern invention, they are a natural concomitant of war, and even if there are no official atrocity story writers, the stories get invented spontaneously in order to maintain the proper spirit of hatred. In any tense situation rumours spread like wildfire, whether officially inspired or just as figments of some particularly vivid imagination.

Humour also plays a part, particularly in an attempt to make the enemy appear ridiculous and silly and, therefore, less frightening. This, as likely as not, is the origin of satire.

I suppose the two distinct arts of encouraging friends and discouraging enemies reached a climax during the last great war. No lie, no terminological inexactitude, no twist of the phrasemaker's talent was missed in the endless attempts to confuse, mislead, to misrepresent the facts or even to tell the truth whenever it was convenient to the purpose. Lord Haw-Haw may have been a bit of a joke, but people listened to him all the same.

Of course, there were those who were not taken in. Even though the fabricated facts and the fraudulent stories were believed with the same old-fashioned zeal by the great majority, many people were consciously aware that a propaganda machine was at work. They realised that everything they were being told could hardly be described as the unvarnished truth. That line about 'our troops have retired to previously prepared positions of greater strength' began to wear a bit thin when people realised that it was meant to cloak what had been, in fact, a resounding defeat.

However, this is really a reflection on the standard of propaganda and I doubt if there will ever be a sufficient proportion of incredulous people to counteract a really competent propaganda campaign.

In the last war speeches of exhortation and abuse of the enemy reached unprecedented proportions because everything was broadcast by radio and the glow of satisfaction created by inspiring words reached a much wider audience at first hand. Furthermore, radio made it possible to broadcast counter-propaganda within the enemy territory, and also to give encouragement to occupied countries.

The leaflet raids carried out during what was called the 'phoney war' period, although designed with laudable intention, were, I think it is generally recognised, peculiarly ineffective. However, later on in the war, leaflets distributed among the German civilian population had quite an appreciable impact.

The important point to remember is that the propaganda of the two Great Wars, although deployed as a weapon by opposing Governments, was rather an amateur affair; it was still used in its original and conventional sense to boost morale at home and to annoy the enemy. In other words, propaganda has always been an adjunct to warfare. In the future, I predict warfare will become an adjunct to propaganda.

With the ending of the fighting, the propaganda organisation, which had been established to assist the military campaigns of the last war, came to an end, but no one could claim that peace had been restored, so the art or practice of propaganda entered an entirely new phase. In fact, propaganda took over as the principal means of conflict, and, because few people were getting killed in the process, the situation became known as the cold war. Instead of trying to force people to abandon the political system under which they were living through the threat of military action and by the conventional process of military occupation, every other means of persuasion was employed.

Clausewitz wrote that 'military power is the extension of national policy'. Today national policy can be equally well extended by propaganda. In any dispute between nations, military power was used to attempt to coerce the other side into accepting your solution to the dispute. That is to say, it was used to create a situation in which the more powerful state could achieve a satisfactory diplomatic and political settlement.

It is important to remember that neither military force nor propaganda can bring about a settlement on its own. Settlements between Governments or between factions can only be made by direct contact through diplomatic channels. Propaganda is the business of trying to influence public and, if necessary, world opinion; diplomacy is the art of negotiation between Governments in private. The diplomatic task is virtually impossible if public and world opinion are opposed to the solution being sought by one or the other side. Diplomatic activity by itself is extremely unlikely to influence public opinion. Suez was a clear case of world opinion defeating both military and political intentions. The Falklands proved the opposite case.

I realise that the word propaganda has a rather sinister ring to it. But, just because we did not like the way Goebbels used it, we should not condemn the whole idea. After all, the worst propaganda conflict is preferable to any limited war and infinitely preferable to hot war.

I would like to suggest that the most important battle and bitter engagement of the twenty-year cold war was fought and won by propaganda. If the Cuban crisis had not been solved by a massive public propaganda offensive, the third and final hot war would have certainly broken out in 1962.

Considering that the immediate cause of the crisis was military, in that the dispute was about the installation of military weapons, this must have been one of the most noteworthy occasions in world history when a military situation has been resolved by means of propaganda designed to influence world opinion, and not by force. The propaganda campaign, which included a masterly performance by Adlai Stevenson in the United Nations, created the necessary atmosphere in which the diplomatic and political negotiations could take place. It is true, of course, that the Russians had no means of forcing their way through the naval blockade, but those who claim that the threat of the use of force really settled the issue should remember that the Russians could only fall back on nuclear weapons, so that the actual use of force would certainly have damaged both sides beyond repair and probably made life of any sort in the rest of the world very unpleasant. The threat of force may discourage aggression, but it cannot contribute to the settlement of a dispute.

Vietnam is another case where the outcome of an armed conflict was decided by propaganda; though, having regard to what has happened since the U.S. withdrawal, it illustrates that successful propaganda has nothing to do with right and wrong. It also demonstrates, in a chilling way, the remarkable power of a propaganda-inspired internal opposition to the policy of a democratically constituted Government.

The interesting point about these cases, and many similar ones, is that the propaganda campaign was planned and conducted by people with little or no connection with the military organisation.

Now, it will be argued that this is just as it should be. The military machine does not understand the process of propaganda and it should have nothing to do with it. The responsibility of the military is to take over when force becomes necessary. Naturally the general conduct of the cold war is the absolute responsibility of the political Government. However, within the cold war there are many individual campaigns.

If normal friendly relations exist between two countries, the threat of force is not necessary and any kind of propaganda cold war is also unnecessary. But say some cause for argument occurs; it may start in official diplomatic circles, it will then spread to newspapers, television and radio either spontaneously or by direction, and gradually a situation of cold war will develop with active military precautionary measures going on at the same time. No overt declaration of hostilities is necessary to begin the participation of military forces. A few tourists, a few infiltrators, perhaps a para-military gang of terrorists may need to be rounded up, perhaps even a leaflet raid may have to be dealt with.

The fact is that there is no hard and fast line where civil propaganda activities cease and where full military action begins. The two activities overlap and run into each other and yet they are under entirely separate direction. What is more, the media, and therefore the principal means for transmitting propaganda in a 'free' country, are normally not under the control of the Government, and virtually no organisation exists to conduct a coherent propaganda campaign, much less to co-ordinate with whatever limited military action is necessary.

Let me give some more examples w. .re propaganda properly used in conjunction with military or semi-military operations could have had, or did have, a decisive influence.

Take the case of Malaya. It became obvious that purely military action by itself could not free the country from terrorists and organised bandits. The situation was only finally restored after a determined propaganda campaign designed to encourage the local population and villagers to play their part. Their response combined with the necessary military action finally proved conclusive.

A particularly interesting example was the extraordinary business of the Indonesian policy of confrontation and the para-military invasion of Malaya and Borneo. It is a well-known characteristic of dictators that, when things are going badly at home, there is nothing like an excursion abroad to raise patriotic enthusiasm. Nothing would have suited Dr Sukarno better than the use of force in retaliation against Indonesia at this point. As with Nasser, it would have strengthened his position at once. However, the point is that an aggressor always lays himself open to a propaganda counter-attack.

Here was the perfect opportunity for the judicious use of offensive propaganda designed to weaken Sukarno's position at home and to marshal world opinion against his efforts to cause trouble with Malaya. The military confrontation was obviously the more spectacular but the ideological confrontation was the more important. This meant that propaganda was also necessary to encourage and inform the people of Malaya and to convince them that they were on the right side.

I think it would be true to say that the so-called 'Hearts and Minds

Campaign' among the tribesmen of Borneo, in which the S.A.S. Regiment played such an important part, had a very considerable influence on the course of events in that island.

Not long after the confrontation I met a young army officer who had been seconded to be Information Officer in Sarawak. I asked him about his responsibilities. He told me that he was required to brief the press and to provide all the necessary information. This competent but untrained captain was the sum total of the propaganda machinery in Sarawak. He did his best but his resources were wholly inadequate. Much later in the proceedings a political advisor was sent to the area but, without the means of transmitting his case, his efforts could be no more effective.

One of the most intriguing cases stemmed from the trouble in Aden and the South Arabian Federation. The point at issue was the acceptance of the Federation as a system of Government for that area. Cynics may say that even the best propaganda could never make federation attractive to anybody; unfortunately, political federation is one of those theories which has much intellectual sympathy but little popular support. However, it is my contention that effective propaganda stood as good a chance of persuading the tribesmen to accept federation as the infinitely more expensive use of military force.

Radio Cairo was particularly active at that time with subversive propaganda, and its broadcasts could be received on every transistor in the Middle East. When the British authorities in Aden asked for a more powerful transmitter for its radio station so as to counteract some of Cairo's broadcasts, the request was turned down – probably on account of the cost. Yet the cost of a transmitter plus studios and staff would have been modest compared to the expenditure on military operations.

Northern Ireland provides an excellent example of one side holding the conventional police and military initiative, and the other side getting away with a devastating propaganda initiative.

There can be little doubt that the Soviet Union operates a most comprehensive propaganda campaign at all times, at all levels and by every conceivable means. It switches from a peace offensive one day to a hatred campaign the next. But it is wide open to counter-attack. The military occupation of neighbouring countries and treatment of Jews and political prisoners in Russia are obviously subjects for exploitation.

At the time of the revolutionary activities in Portugal in 1974, the communist propaganda offensive was on a massive scale. During the whole period there was a torrent of communist propaganda, hatred and revenge. Communist songs on the radio woke people up; the newspapers were full of it; all the arts were dominated by Communism; and the bookshops were full of communist literature carefully translated into Portuguese. At the time it seemed that it could not fail, but fortunately the tide was turned by the good sense of the Portuguese.

Once the military operation begins, propaganda can only act in a supporting role, but effective propaganda at the right time might conceivably prevent military operations from becoming necessary.

Incidentally, there are two very important points to remember about propaganda. In the first place, unlike military force which can only hurt and destroy, propaganda can be used to make friends as well as to denounce enemies; it can incite but it can also pacify; it can be subversive but it can also be patriotic. Secondly, propaganda campaigns can be conducted anywhere in the world without the normal restraints of geography or lines of communication which limit conventional warfare. The Portuguese case illustrates this very clearly.

It may have been true of the caveman that he got his wife by clubbing her into agreement, but today the art of making love, which, at any rate in the preliminary stages, is the art of persuasion, has reached a very advanced state indeed. The creation of international friendship by deliberate propaganda might be equally effective in achieving a desired result. At any rate it would be a change from the use of threats and force which are the only arguments we have ever tried to use so far.

Then again, the psychology of mankind is far better understood today than ever before. All the primitive emotional mechanisms which produce fear, anger, hatred, respect, love or loyalty have been exposed. So far, however, the only people who use this knowledge deliberately, apart from certain political groups, are successful public relations consultants, personnel management departments, and advertising agents.

In some instances the means of communicating the desired information to the public already exists and is in the hands of profit-seeking private enterprise. The problem here is to persuade these news media to use the propaganda information, or at least to present it to them in such a way that they cannot ignore it. This is a case of straightforward public relations work. Where the news media are, so to speak, in 'hostile' hands – by that I mean under the control of the other side – the problem is somewhat more difficult, but even then the position is not entirely hopeless.

However, in such cases as the South Arabian Federation or Malaya, the means of conveying the necessary information locally was almost entirely absent; therefore any attempt to make use of propaganda would have meant the direct operation of news media and other facilities set up for the purpose.

This is not an original idea. In the last war Allied Supreme Commanders had complete propaganda departments within their commands which they operated with guidance from the political Governments in London and Washington. The Germans went further and established uniformed propaganda companies attached to particular army commands but under the direct control of the Ministry of Propaganda. In both cases legitimate as well as clandestine methods were used to get the information and the stories across to the other side.

In fact we tried to do the same thing in a different way. In 1941 the Political Warfare Executive was created, initially under a committee composed of representatives of the B.B.C., the Ministry of Information and the Special Operations Executive. In 1942 it was put in the charge of Bruce Lockhart as Director General, with a Royal Marine Brigadier, Dallas Brooks, as Deputy Director and in executive command. Both S.H.A.P.E. and S.E.A.C. had their own Psychological Warfare Divisions.

Any nation which uses this extra weapon as a part of its armoury is in a position to operate a much more flexible policy. In addition to its traditional threat to use force it should also be able to bring either an offensive or defensive propaganda campaign into being, and therefore, in the classical conception of warfare, it would be able to practise the maximum economy of effort with a wider choice of means to achieve the aim.

I think it is worth remembering that ever since primitive times, and even now among animals, the whole intention of warlike preparation, or in the case of animals the display of aggressiveness, is for one protagonist to force the other to accept his will with the absolute minimum use of violence. Many animals are extremely aggressive and argumentative, particuarly over matters of territory, but it is very seldom that a fight reaches really serious proportions. In most cases one or the other recognises the weakness of his position and gives up at once, and lives to fight another day. The conception of unconditional surrender as an end in itself is contrary to all experience of nature and history. In 1939–1945 it merely served to distract everybody from the principal object of the war, which was the destruction of Hitler's government and party, and did nothing to secure the freedom of Poland which was, after all, the original cause of the outbreak.

Where an opponent can be convinced by persuasion, flattery or enticement to change his point of view, the result is likely to be much more satisfactory in the long run than if his mind has to be changed, and then probably only temporarily, by force.

Of course, it depends how you do it. The Japanese tried shouting 'Death to Roosevelt' at their American opponents, only to get the answer 'Delighted to hear you are a fellow Republican'.

FOUR

On Being in Two Minds

GENERATIONS OF philosophers, scholars, scientists and engineers have used their brains with brilliant effect to the benefit of mankind. Many of them must have wondered how their brains worked and several of them made substantial contributions to the understanding of human thought processes and behaviour. But it is only in recent years that the structure and chemistry of the human brain has begun to be unravelled. This process has coincided with the development of research into what has come to be known as artificial intelligence made possible and stimulated by the rapidly growing computer technology.

One of the evident characteristics of computers is that, so far at least, they are unencumbered with any kind of emotion or aesthetic judgement. Their great advantage is that their responses are, or at least are intended to be, entirely rational, whether they are engaged in playing games, recognising features, correcting grammar or translating from the Chinese. They do not get angry if they are asked silly questions and they do not make guesses if they do not know the answer. Neither are they liable to any prejudice that is not programmed into them.

It seems therefore as if there is still a major difference between the function of the human brain and that of the computer.

The most obvious difference is that human thought and behaviour appear to be governed by two frequently conflicting influences. Freud postulated the conscious and the unconscious mind but it could be that the physical structure of the brain may contain part of the explanation.

Rather than pretend that I know anything about the structure of the brain, let me quote from a book entitled *Archetype* by Anthony Stevens, a practising psychiatrist. He writes: 'If you take a human brain in your hands and examine it, the first thing that will strike you is that the greater portion of it is divided into two parts. These are the cerebral hemispheres, man's main claim to fame. For many centuries this arrangement stimulated curiosity and raised the question whether these two parts perform different functions. The first indication that they do was noted by the ancient Egyptians, who observed that brain injury on one side can result in paralysis on the other. This intriguing "cross-over" of function was confirmed by neurologists in the nineteenth century . . .' He continues: 'It is well established that both cerebral hemispheres are concerned with contra-lateral movements and sensations. But what of psychic functions? Could there be any differences in mental functioning between the left and right sides of the brain?'

As you can well imagine, a great deal of information on malfunctions was gathered after the First World War. To quote Stevens again: 'When this evidence was collected it established beyond doubt that a number of functions were primarily represented on different sides of the brain: damage to the left side resulted in impairment of speech, difficulties in reading and deterioration in the ability to do mental arithmetic and use of logical thought, while damage to the right side caused a deficit in visio-spatial capacities such as those required to dress oneself, find one's way around a hospital ward, and recognise patterns. On the whole, damage to the left cerebral hemisphere appeared to cause more serious incapacity than damage to the right, and this led to the conclusion that the left hemisphere is normally "dominant" over the right "sub-dominant" hemisphere.'

To put it simply, the left brain controls your ability to speak and to count, while the right brain decides what you say and what procedure to use in the solution of mathematical problems. This explains why some highly trained intellectuals seem to have such poor judgement.

Stevens then goes on to say: 'Cerebral dominance, like all biologically determined human characteristics is susceptible to environmental in-fluences. It is probable that in all cultures the left hemisphere of individual men and women, with few exceptions, dominates over the right; but it is equally likely that in some cultures it is more dominant than in others. Our own culture is a case in point: ever since the Renaissance, stress has increasingly been laid on the need to develop left hemispheric functions at the expense of the right. Encouragement of the left hemisphere begins early in life with the emphasis placed in all Western primary schools on the need for proficiency in the three R's (reading, writing and arithmetic). Although right hemispheric activities such as art, drama, dancing and music, are given a place in the curriculum, fewer resources and fewer hours are allocated to them than to left-sided disciplines such as mathematics, languages, physics and chemistry.' It is of course much easier to set objective examinations in the left-sided disciplines.

One of the obvious consequences of this emphasis on the development of the left brain is the emergence of materialist ideologies and the concept that human behaviour can be reduced to a sort of machine-like rationality. Not long ago I noticed a passage in an article about establishing the credit-rating of borrowers by a questionnaire system. The article included this passage:

'. . . the problem with credit scoring is that, having put people in categories, it treats everyone in the same category alike. It may be true, statistically, that young single tenants are in general more likely to be bad payers than older married home-owners – but it is certainly not true of each and every one of them. You may share a number of characteristics with people in "bad risk" categories, while being an impeccable character yourself.'

Statistics and rational arguments have their value but when applied to people they are useless if they ignore the right-sided factors in the make-up of individuals.

I think that is sufficient to describe the functions and the influence of the two hemispheres of the brain. The essential point is that the left hemisphere controls the rational and analytic functions, while the right originates the emotions and the aesthetic functions. But there is a third element in the brain that plays a very important part in its function. This is the bridge of nerves – about 200 million of them – that connects the two hemispheres, the so-called cerebral commissure or corpus callosum. Research has made it possible to deduce that the corpus acts as a means of allowing the two hemispheres to co-operate so that conceived thoughts can be expressed in speech or in writing. It also acts to resolve conflicts, or at least to allow any excesses by one hemisphere to be modified by the other, provided that both sides have been more or less equally developed. The corpus does not initiate any thoughts or sensations and if the two halves of the brain become hopelessly incompatible, as in cases of severe epilepsy, the corpus can be severed to relieve the condition without doing any serious damage to the personality.

Quite apart from this divided responsibility in the brain, since time immemorial people have thought of themselves as having a body and a separate soul; in other words, there is a difference between the physical brain and the mind. Most people at some time or other experience the sensation of separation or distinction between themselves and their bodies. We know that the brain is a physical entity, we feel that the mind or the soul is the unique personality created by the functioning of the brain.

It so happens that this division has a close analogy with electronic computers. Without my going into the basic principles of construction, such machines consist of a series of interconnected structural entities – memory, central processor, control, peripherals – each having a functional purpose irrespective of who designed the parts or constructed the whole machine. The machine is made to work by an operator who tries to get it to behave in a certain way by giving it a suitable combination of memories, that is stored data; instructions, known as the program; and stimuli, which are the inputs to the peripherals.

In computer jargon the material fed into the machine is called the software. Change the software and the computer, in using its new stored data and program, will solve a different series of problems: it will behave differently.

Dr Gosling of Plessey puts it this way: 'The same software in a physically different machine will evoke the same pattern of behaviour. On the other hand one machine takes on many "identities" depending on the software currently in use. The computing system "is" the software much more than the hardware (that is the equipment) so far as behaviour is concerned.' He then asks the question: 'How does this help the problem of giving modern meaning to the ancient concept of soul? Simply, it restores that concept to full vigour. The body is the hardware, the software is the soul.'

And he goes on:

'If my brain can be likened to a biological super-computer, then it can only function by virtue of the incredibly sophisticated adaptive software which is stored within it. In a proper sense it is this software which defines my identity, and hence is me. It consists of all my memories together with a vast ordered listing of statements about behaviour, most of them conditional on stimuli, and it is because I have this software within me that my behaviour is consistent enough for me to have a recognisable personality. When my friends recognise me from my words and deeds, my views, what I write, it is my software that they are greeting.'

Of course the biological super-computer to which he refers is not exactly comparable to the hardware of an electronic computer. Like any other biological structure it is subject to the rules of genetics in the way it functions and it also inherits some software in the form of instincts.

It may well be that scientific research into the function of the human brain in the future may reveal a great deal more about ourselves, but I think there is quite a lot to be deduced from our present knowledge.

For instance, Stevens mentioned the emphasis on the development of left brain and the neglect of the right brain activities in schools. If the left brain is dominant anyway, it means that it can effectively block whatever modifying influence the right brain might have on behaviour. Left-sided analysis may be excellent but if right-sided judgement is poor the result is useless. Equally, if right brain activity has never been deliberately developed then right brain-originated behaviour is liable to be erratic and unbalanced. This might well explain how it is that, although educational levels have risen dramatically in the last fifty years, so has juvenile crime, and moral behavioural standards also seem to have declined. Furthermore, as the right brain has not been programmed with any what might be called civilised software, it remains receptive to any software program that might be plugged into it. This could explain the extraordinary success of so many quasi-religions and aggressive ideological cults in capturing young converts.

They are sometimes described as having been brain-washed but that is not an appropriate expression. You do not need to wipe a clean slate, you just write your own message on the blank space. During the Korean war, quite a large number of American prisoners were successfully 'brain-washed': the blank in their right hemisphere was filled by Marxist doctrine. On the other hand their captors had no success at all with the Turkish prisoners with strong religious and military traditions who stuck together and resisted all attempts to reprogram their principles.

Christian martyrs and patriotic resistance fighters are other examples of the power of a right-brain program to withstand the most violent assaults on the body. There are also any number of examples of political prisoners who have asserted that their religious convictions gave them the strength and resolution to survive everything their torturers could do to them.

The question of course arises: what program should we be putting into the right brains of our children? There seem to be two opposing attitudes. At one end of the spectrum are the dedicated ideologists who are determined to get their particular program in at almost any cost. This is not brain-washing but more like brain-pollution. At the opposite end are those who maintain that every child should have the right to write its own program for its right brain. But this is not really an option at all because it means that, with the inevitable volume of input into the left brain, the child grows up with a lopsided personality. This, as I have already pointed out, can result in either unbalanced erratic behaviour or the possibility of being taken over by some weird or even sinister cult program. In either case there is always the chance that the right brain activity becomes so strong that, even when there is no stress, the rational part of the left brain no longer exerts any influence and the person becomes a fanatic or a zealot. Under stress such a person would be liable to panic and hysteria.

It might well be argued that demonstrations, protests, the moronic chanting of slogans, crime, violence, drug taking, alcoholism, terrorism, addiction to peculiar cults or even bureaucratic bullying under a dictatorship, all stem from lack of judgement due to the void in the right brain program.

Between these two extremes there still exist those who believe in learning from the experience of previous generations. They recognise that something has to be done to develop the right brain but in such a way that a person does not become so dependent on an emotional attachment to a cult or ideology as to warp their personality or judgement. The sort of program they seek to input, apart from experience of the arts and an introduction to religious and moral concepts, combines an appreciation of the civilised values of loyalty, honesty and integrity with exposure to both the good and the bad in human nature, so that the advantages of humanity, compassion, tolerance and co-operation over conflict and hatred become apparent. The object might be stated to be a software program that will allow the person to react to any situation or stimulus in a civilised manner, and to resist corruption, subversion, panic and hysteria even under stress.

It must be said that, even with a balanced development of both halves of the brain, there is always a chance that an example of the catastrophe theory may take place. The theory is based on the observation that conversion of one state of being to another is not always a gradual process. In many cases increasing stress may not appear to have much effect until there is a sudden breakdown or catastrophe. For instance, if you try to break a dry wooden stick, increasing pressure starts to bend the stick and then suddenly it breaks completely. A very good example of this is St Paul's sudden conversion on the road to Damascus. All his left-sided functions continued as before, but the messages coming from his right brain had undergone a complete transformation. This is not unusual, in fact it is something that must have happened to those who claim to have been born again. Most dissidents in Marxist countries must have had a similar experience, possibly as a result of the left-sided analytical frustration with a system that may be rational in theory but unacceptable in practice.

The Armed Services are a good example of the empirical approach. Experience has shown that success in battle depends upon a great deal more than weapons and the left brain functional ability to handle them effectively. The right brain functions of loyalty and co-operation within a unit, the will to endure, effective leadership, readiness to follow, resistance to panic and a belief in the cause are equally if not more important. A number of very effective ways have been developed over the centuries by the Services to program the right brain to these ends. The tribal quality of the regimental system, the emphasis on tradition, ceremonies linked with the colours, regimental memorial days, inter-unit sports competitions, adventure training, simulated battle experience, they each play their part in building up the right brain function to complement the practical function of the left. The purpose is also to ensure that, even under the severe stresses of war, men can still retain a calm humanity, loyalty to their cause, a balance between the rational need to defeat the enemy using minimum force and a right brain conditioned to suppress hatred and revenge in favour of humanity and compassion.

Returning to artificial intelligence, there can be little doubt that computers at the moment only have one lobe to their brains and that it corresponds more or less to the left lobe of the human brain. Consequently it is only capable of coping with the rational and the logical. However, as computers become progressively more sophisticated and their ability to make judgements develops, it may well be that prejudice in some form or other may creep into their behaviour. It might happen that as the preparation of their software becomes more complex so the influence of the programmers' right brain will find its way into the program and thereby impart prejudice to the behaviour of the machine, or even encourage it to develop its own.

It also raises the possibility that someone is already creating an electronic copy of the brain by designing a computer with two lobes connected by a corpus callosum. One half of the computer would be given the normal rational program while the other half might be given software programmed to react to a different set of stimuli modelled on, say, party political prejudice, vested interest groups, or even known racial or national characteristics. Perhaps such a machine would also produce the first case of electronic apoplexy.

FIVE

Prejudice, Malice and Sacred Cows

NO SOCIETY that values its liberty can do without the freedom to report on, comment on, discuss and indeed to gossip about people, institutions and events. I have yet to come across a Society, free or otherwise, that seems to be short of volunteers to make speeches, give lectures, write for the press, perform for radio or television, or, if all else fails, to write letters to the editor. Some do it for a living, others do it because they feel the need to complain, enlighten, inform or persuade their fellow citizens, and there are some who do it because they are invited. The flattery of the invitation is usually enough to overcome any fear or reluctance to accept. Talent is seldom a serious consideration.

The remarkable part of all this is that there are, apparently, a sufficient number of people 'out there' among the public who are prepared not just to put up with it all, but to go on asking for more.

But, for all this insatiable demand, there are several snags and pitfalls in trying to communicate with the public. The trouble is that so many subjects are mined with prejudice or festooned with the barbed wire entanglement of political and economic factional dogma. If you don't tread on a tender C.B.I. corn you are likely to kick a union bunion, and there is always the risk of setting off a party political booby-trap.

I find that you have to be particularly careful when the country is going through one of those periods of economic crisis (although they are hardly periods any more – the only let-up seems to be when the major political organisations are undergoing such internal ructions that they are temporarily diverted from the national issues). At such times the air becomes blue with the cross-fire of accusation and denial, blame and excuse, claim and counter-claim, salvoes of statistics, barrages of analyses, and economists sniping at each other from entrenched positions. Causes are confused with symptoms, solutions are advanced for unidentified problems, and theories are treated like relics of the True Cross in the Middle Ages. On top of all this, there seems to be a positive relish in the prediction of doom and disaster, and any reported rise in the number of unemployed is greeted by some with undisguised delight. Violence and terrorism are front-page news.

Harping on disaster may be realistic but it cannot be good for national morale. From a listener's, or reader's, point of view there is nothing more deadly than having to sit through endless regurgitations of the currently fashionable comments on what are deemed to be the issues of the day. Worse still is the use of jargon phrases in an effort to sound well-informed. U-turns, social justice, political solution, inner city decay, deprivation. They and many like them may have had some meaning in an original article, but they have long since become symbol phrases, used to appear up-to-date but in such a way that they have no particular meaning. They have become latter-day clichés, listened to more or less politely like the recitation of well-known prayers.

There are, needless to say, any number of dedicated researchers, painstaking lecturers, objective reporters, chat-show experts, brilliant investigative journalists and comprehensible economists. There are even a few gossip writers with a sense of humour and humanity. But paragons are few and far between in any walk of life and for both amateurs and professionals the pressures and temptations, inherent in the business of communicating ideas to the public, can hardly be conducive to a monk-like renunciation of all self-indulgence. What is more, there are a lot of people who do not really like the truth; they prefer what they like to believe.

It is so tempting to allow a little prejudice to slip in or to indulge in a bit of malice, instead of trying to stick to the whole truth. Anyone who puts pen to paper or voice on tape for public consumption is bound to include something of his or her own personality. It is probably a determination to be totally impersonal, and hence hopefully untraceable, that drives bureaucrats to compose their material in gobbledygook. The difficulty about allowing personality in is that not all personal characteristics are necessarily as attractive to others as they may be to oneself. It is a risk that has to be taken, but at least all but the naive and totally unselfconscious do make an effort to suppress or to disguise what they know to be the less amiable features of their character.

It is never easy getting facts right in the first place, it is more difficult to present them unambiguously, and more difficult still to draw the proper conclusions from them. All the more so if there is a case to be proved, in which event the resulting distortion is probably unintentional and could be excused as over-enthusiasm. On the other hand, facts can easily be distorted by prejudice or malice. Prejudice is usually a case of 'my mind is made up, don't confuse me with the facts' and therefore virtually sub-conscious. Malice on the other hand leads to deliberate misconstruction. Undesirable though this may be, the trouble is that prejudice and malice are all too frequently remarkably popular, so that it is not surprising to find some professionals turning them to commercial advantage.

Prejudice and malice are not the only causes of distortion. It is just as easy to mislead by selection. This can be the result of one of two characteristics: pre-conception, or an inability to comprehend a novel idea. Pre-conception is a consequence of a desire to type-cast or pigeon-hole a character or a subject. It probably stems from the all too frequent and rather lazy tendency of economists to reduce everything to gener-alisations. There are no people any more, they simply get lumped together as industry, workers, capitalists, fascists, or any other convenient label. The danger, of course, is that it works the other way as well. If, for instance, certain characteristics are imputed to 'the press', it is difficult not to assume that those characteristics are shared by every individual 'press man'. If that happens then it follows that whatever the individual says or does it is pre-conceived that his motives and his general outlook are the same as those attributed to his group as a whole. Consequently, anything he produces which does not conform to this pre-conception is either ignored or treated as shockingly unconventional, even though it may be something quite happily accepted from a member of a different group. The shock and the horror are not due to what is said or done but to the alarming fact that it was said or done by someone belonging to a group that pre-conception dictates does not say or do such things.

Pre-conception can also derive from popular folklore. Frenchmen eat frogs, all Chinese look alike, they are always having revolutions in South America, these are only a few examples of this form of distortion.

The almost universal reaction to an incomprehensible idea is to ignore it, presumably in the hope that it will go away. When Captain Cook pulled the *Endeavour* up on to a beach on the Australian coast in order to effect repairs, he noticed that some native fishermen, not far away, continued their activities without even looking around at what must have been the equivalent of the landing of a flying saucer. The argument seems to be that if there is no explanation – which is the same as saying that it is incomprehensible – then it cannot exist. Indeed, this is precisely the attitude of many people, scientists included, to the idea of flying saucers and other U.F.O.s reported by otherwise entirely trustworthy witnesses.

Distortion can also be the result of assuming that others have the same standards and reactions as your own. It is the exact reverse of putting yourself in someone else's shoes. What you are doing is putting them in your shoes, and the chances are that they do not fit. The trouble is that so much reporting depends on observation and inference, with the result that ascribing the wrong motive or reaction creates a wholly misleading conclusion.

One of the most powerful of human instincts is competition, and consequently aggression. This is usually taken to find expression in commerce and politics and particularly in sport. At least in sport the competition takes place within strictly defined and enforced rules, and the aggression is kept within reasonable limits. There is competition for circulation in the press as well as for viewers and listeners. But just because there is no overt competition in the more intellectual pursuits does not mean that communicators do not have any aggressive instincts. Whoever said that the 'pen is mightier than the sword' put it very neatly. The sword is designed as an instrument of physical aggression but when the pen is used aggressively against another person it assaults the mind and the damage it can do is probably even greater. Physical wounds can at least be healed but, apart from the laws of libel and slander, there is little protection and virtually no treatment for damage inflicted on the mind. There is not much future in challenging the great with a sword, but it is very easy to make them look small with a pen, and the action gives the small a wonderful feeling of being great.

I do not want to suggest that every forceful communicator is using his 'pen' as a means of working off his aggression, which would be as unfair as to suggest that every schoolmaster who ever wielded a cane was a sadistic sex fiend. On the other hand, my impression is that there are some people who either cannot or do not wish to work off their aggression through some form of recreation or competitive activity and prefer to take it out on their fellow creatures through the means of communication with the public. I am no psychologist but it seems to me that this form of aggression against individuals or groups, such as Hitler's hysterical prejudice against the Jews, Marx's constant abuse of the middle class or the ferocity of the attacks by some religious leaders against other sects or religions, betrays a serious flaw in the character, to put it mildly. It is unpleasant in itself and it can have frighteningly dangerous consequences.

Aggression by the pen can take various forms. The right sort of publication will often give space for material directed at the right sort of target. On the other hand, unconventional artists have provided wonderful opportunities for some extremely aggressive critics. This type of aggression is also particularly satisfactory as the victim can seldom if ever get his own back. The critics are always going to win anyway because it is the creative artist who has to put his head on the block by making some sort of statement with his creation. All the critic has to do is to bring the chopper down. I cannot imagine anyone likes to be called a 'decadent bourgeois' even if he does not know what it means. He should not really worry as anyone using such clichés is doing more to expose his own intellectual limitations than to offer valid criticism.

The trouble with this sort of aggressive criticism is that most artists are trying to earn a living and not unnaturally they suppose that a good review will help their prospects. The consequence is that some may be tempted to react by producing work designed to please the critics or to demonstrate that they do not deserve the label 'fascist lackey' or 'hopeless reactionary'. Unfortunately, experience has shown that they are heading into a cul de sac because, so long as there is anything remotely recognisable or figurative in the work, the aggressive critic will find it and pounce on it like a cat on a mouse. All that is left to the artist is to become progressively more abstract and with each step to challenge the critic to find something to criticise. The artist eventually wins game, set and match by producing a totally monochrome canvas.

The pen is probably at its most aggressive in politics. There is in the politically 'free' world the usual in-fighting between those who do not agree with each other or cannot tolerate the other's party. This is good dirty knock-about stuff conducted by people who relish it as much as back row forwards in Rugby and who are as often firm friends off the pitch. The danger arises when it is taken seriously and turned into physical violence by their followers.

In one-party systems, on the other hand, the internal conflict between rivals and the external aggression against 'the enemy' is conducted with all the stately formality of an eighteenth-century gavotte. The style and language never vary, the pitch of hysteria never falters and the arguments have all the novelty of stale buns. Perhaps this is not altogether surprising, considering the fate in store for those who disagree with the party line.

I find one of the great hazards of communicating with the public is the existence of certain taboo subjects. According to the New English Bible, St Paul in his first letter to the Corinthians wrote, 'You say, "we are free to do anything", but is everything good for you?' Things have not changed much. We pride ourselves on having freedom of speech and it is true theoretically, but I consider it very unwise to take this too literally. We pride ourselves on having got rid of what are called Victorian taboos but all that means in practice is that some people can indulge their taste for adolescent pornography in public without being criticised. In fact the taboo is now on the other foot – as it were – it is now the critic of public pornography that has to watch what he or, more to the point, what she says.

Taboos are most problematic for anyone required to speak in public. Writing for public consumption on the other hand is not quite so hazardous. Perhaps this has something to do with the idea that, if you are present when someone is speaking, you are more or less bound to listen, and of course you listen more attentively if they say something with which you do not agree. On the other hand, if you pick up a book or see an article in print you have the option of not reading it. Somehow the act of deliberately not reading something can give you the feeling that it has been erased or never really written in the first place. If Mr Enoch Powell had confined himself to *writing* his views on racial problems, I doubt very much whether anyone outside a small circle of sympathisers would have heard of them. The suggestion has been made that, while the Victorians were prudes about sex, the present generation is prudish about politics. This may account for the fact that so many taboos are closely related to sacred cows. A good example would be the United Nations. The motives of those who devised it and the intentions of those who put it into practice are obviously above reproach, but like any utopian concept it was bound to have weaknesses and anomalies in practice. But, such is the Pavlovian reaction to the slightest comment about the United Nations or its agencies that, except by politicians, the subject is best left alone. I suppose the same was true once upon a time of religion, but if the 'trendy' reformers are anything to go by, some are better maintained, lest worse should befall.

Bitter experience has taught me that one of the most important rules to remember is that a minority must never criticise or, still more dangerous, ever make fun of a majority. I always remember a cartoon in *Punch* many years ago. It was in two parts. The top picture showed a group of people laughing their heads off at a man slipping on a banana skin. The lower picture showed the opposite, the whole group all slipping on banana skins while the lone spectator of this even funnier sight was shown slinking away, presumably in fear of being beaten up by the others for laughing at them. Incidentally, the 'press' must always be taken deadly seriously.

The peculiar feature of these taboos is that some are only taboos to one group of people while they can be safely knocked by another. I would like to give some examples but I fear all the best ones are taboo subjects for me. Comics and satirical programmes can knock everything, or almost everything. I suspect that even their licence is limited by some taboos. Commercial radio and television are probably more conscious about offending the audience than the B.B.C., safe, or fairly safe, behind its licence money. It is also a reasonable bet that indiscreet or scurrilous public comments about the proprietor or his friends are taboo in most media organisations.

The common denominator of all taboos seems to be the general acceptance that some institution or doctrine somehow embodies ultimate truth and should consequently not be questioned. Picasso and the Gleneagles Agreement, the Tate Gallery and the G.L.C., Council housing and the Health Service: anyone unwise enough to voice serious criticism of institutions such as these runs a grave risk of being branded a dangerous lunatic. H. C. Andersen wrote the definitive treatise on sacred cows in a little story about 'The Emperor's Clothes'. As he points out, anyone who wants to make a favourable impression has to reinforce the taboo by paying tribute to the currently reigning sacred cows, even though such slavish toeing of the conventional line frequently results in blatant hypocrisy. I was once congratulated by a women's organisation for supposedly refusing to dine at an exclusively male club.

Nowhere is this ritual feeding of sacred cows taken to such extremes as in the Comrade countries. Indeed, they reserve a distinctive rhetoric specially for the purpose which makes it sound even less sincere than it may be intended to be. The consequence is that their people have to become schizophrenic in their attitudes. There is what they know to be real and true, and they also know what they are expected to say in public. Fortunately, there is evidence that many of the ordinary people can see that this has its funny side and make marvellous jokes about their situation. I assume detection is a taboo subject in a Comrade country, but a joke gets around it. Like this question: 'What is a Polish string quartet?' Answer: 'A Polish symphony orchestra on return from a tour abroad.'

The fact is that sacred cows thrive on being taken seriously, they cannot stand being laughed at.

SIX

Naive Economics

MR MICAWBER'S view of economics was delightfully simple: 'Annual income £20, annual expenditure £19.19 and 6d, result, happiness. Annual income £20, annual expenditure £20 nought and 6d, result, misery.' It may be naive but practically every family and most businesses today would recognise the core of truth in what he said.

The trouble is that, while families and the smaller businesses have to respect the simple rules of naive economics, Governments allow themselves to operate under the rather vague rules of what they like to think is 'sophisticated' economics. These rules are vague because Governments all over the world tend to employ sophisticated economists who can be relied upon to make up the rules as they go along; and, of course, they can also behave like Humpty Dumpty and make words mean whatever they want them to mean. For example, the naive economist might well ask why it is that the tight control of the supply of money in order to prevent inflation is known as 'monetarism', whereas the loose control of the money supply with the consequent debasement of the currency is not monetarism but 'alternative economic policy' or some such description, even though it cannot entirely disregard the quantity of money.

Under sophisticated economic rules it seems that the bigger the organisation the easier it is to fudge the fact of bankruptcy. Thus, individuals and small businesses can go bankrupt all too easily. When bigger businesses get into financial difficulties, the Government simply takes them over. If major cities are faced with the inevitable consequences of mismanagement they have to be rescued or at least kept from complete collapse. When a nation gets into such a situation, whether it has a free enterprise, mixed or planned economy, the position is reversed: it is the banks, from whom it has borrowed money, that are likely to face collapse.

In his day Mr Micawber did not have to cope with the problems of personal taxation. It is rather difficult to imagine how he would have reacted, were he alive today, and had discovered that his income is now taxed before he can think of spending it. Furthermore, if his income is derived from his own savings, it is liable to be taxed at a higher rate than if it comes from an employer. Since Dickens gave him a perceptive insight into economic principles, as the quotation makes clear, it is not beyond the bounds of imagination to assume that Micawber understood how it was possible for him to receive an annual income from a capital sum invested directly or indirectly in company shares or lent to the Government through the purchase of Government securities. What he might well not understand is the logic of sophisticated economics which requires Governments to try to persuade citizens to save and invest their money, while at the same time applying a progressive rate of tax on those who are silly enough, or whose parents were silly enough, to do just that. He would certainly be surprised to discover that if he spent his savings to avoid taxation rather than lend them to industry he would be accused of a malicious 'investment strike'.

Having thus been discouraged from saving so as to provide himself with an income in his old age, it is not altogether surprising to find that he has to rely on a state pension on retirement and quite naturally complains that it is not enough, and that he is likely to lose it if he takes a job. Whereupon, the vicious circle starts again as Governments have to raise more revenue to pay a more adequate, but never 'adequate', pension.

If part of Mr Micawber's income was derived from inherited savings, he would now very soon discover that sophisticated economics rules that it is highly immoral for him to enjoy such 'unearned' favours, even though such an independent income could give him the chance to do useful social or charitable work without having to be paid for it.

Whether income from savings, inherited or not, is immoral is another question but, even if it were, there must be a better way of taxing savings so as not to discourage the accumulation and investment of wealth in job-creating industrial or commercial enterprises. One possible solution might be to have an age-related tax on income from savings in such a way that the rate of tax would be reduced as the taxpayer got older. It might start at 100 per cent at birth for anyone inheriting a fortune and reduce by some percentage each year so that at, say, sixty it would have dropped to 20 per cent and progressively decrease by 1 per cent per year thereafter.

By the taxing of inherited income at a higher rate, personal savings would be encouraged because the sum saved would become progressively more valuable as the saver aged and became progressively less re-employable. It would also put more disposable income into the hands of maturer citizens who might be relied upon not to spend it quite so frivolously as the young.

Since Mr Micawber's income was derived from commissions, he would soon discover that he also had to pay a progressive rate of tax on his earned income. At least that is what the sophisticated economists believe. The naive economist would argue that, when it comes to accepting or negotiating a commission or a wage or salary, no one is particularly interested in the gross figure. What matters is the net sum, or take-home pay.

Consequently, taxes levied on earned incomes are, like the national insurance surcharge, borne by the employer whether he can afford it or not. In 1980 it cost an employer over £100 a week to pay an employee £70 to take home. After all, if the employer did not employ the man and pay him a wage or salary, there would be nothing to tax. Considering that the Government is the largest single employer in the country, and has to pay for this elaborate tax system, it strikes the naive economist as rather strange that the Government should make it so expensive for itself to employ people. Furthermore, even in so-called 'planned economies' there is a differential in the wages and salaries between the less and the more skilled or experienced. By superimposing a progressive tax system, which they have to pay themselves anyway, Governments are also inflating their own wage and salary bills because the curve of the gross differential has to be much steeper, to compensate for the progressive tax rates, in order to arrive at an acceptable curve for the net differential.

However, sophisticated economists seem to be a bit uncertain about this system, or, more likely, as they are probably in one of the higher tax brackets themselves, they find the system rather oppressive. But, instead of admitting the nonsense, they have invented allowances against tax for such things as mortgages, insurance and pension fund contributions. Splendid, but to the naive economist this looks suspiciously like fulfilling the passage in the 19th Chapter of St Luke, where Jesus tells his disciples, 'The man who has will always be given more; but the man who has not will forfeit even what he has.' The trick about allowances is that you have to be able to afford the expenditure before you can claim the allowance and not infrequently the bigger the expenditure the bigger the allowance. As Jesus might have pointed out, the man who has not falls into the poverty trap. The remarkable thing about this whole complicated arrangement is that at the end of the day the Treasury only collects an average of 18 per cent on all wages and salaries paid to employees. The difference between that 18 per cent and the tax rates in each bracket is made up by allowances against tax. This implies that a flat rate tax paid by employers on all wages and salaries of about 18 per cent without any allowance would raise the same total revenue. In fact, it would probably raise much more because the inducement for workers to earn more would be that much greater.

If Mr Micawber had an income derived neither from savings nor from earnings he would, quite reasonably, be entitled to all the unemployment and supplementary benefits. If, as seems fairly likely, Mr Micawber was not over-enthusiastic about getting a regular job and, as is even more likely, many available jobs or opportunities for individual initiative were not to his liking, the system operates even more perversely. Thus, in order to make him significantly better off, an employer would have to offer him a net wage sufficient to yield take-home pay high enough to offset what he gets while unemployed plus the trouble and expense of putting in a full working week. As Mr Micawber is not obviously enthusiastic about regular work, and there is little evidence to suggest that he has any particular skills or talents, such an employer is understandably hard to find.

This awkward dilemma seems to have become apparent since the M.S.C. was created with the main purpose of reducing the cost to the employer of employing people. Having taxed people out of jobs, Governments try to subsidise them back into employment. But then most M.S.C. schemes are to do with the young employed so that Mr Micawber would be unlikely to benefit from them. But should – by some outrageous chance – a friend offer him a job out of kindness of heart, and should this friend subsequently run into financial difficulties, he would find it extremely difficult to make Mr Micawber redundant against Mr Micawber's will. And, if that considerate employer ever regained his prosperity, it would not be unreasonable to assume that he would not be quite so philanthropic a second time.

One of the many peculiar characteristics of sophisticated economists is their inability to make up their minds. Taxes are heaped on to companies, presumably because they are part of the capitalist system, only to be mitigated by allowances and grants to alleviate the resulting social damage.

The consequent complications are endless, but the system appears to have been so worked out – to say devised suggests it was done on purpose and that would be a gross libel since no one in their senses could have deliberately devised such a system – that, while it benefits expanding companies, the companies most adversely affected are those in decline, possibly only temporarily, unless of course they happen to be nationalised.

This schizophrenia seems to derive from the Marxist doctrine of the evils of capitalism which demands that entrepreneurs should be penalised for their initiative, counterbalanced by a vague appreciation that industrial activity has something to do with national economic success. It is like people who are quite content to buy meat from a butcher's shop, but do not approve of the idea of animals being killed. However, schizophrenia of this kind can seldom withstand the temptations of self-interest. The middle-class activities, such as the arts, so popular with sophisticated economists, are given massive hand-outs, while the simpler pleasures of the less sophisticated, like sport, are expected to pay taxes at a far higher rate than they get back in grants.

There is little doubt that the period during which Dickens wrote his novels was a very difficult one for the poor. But at least it was well understood that initiative and enterprise earned its rewards, and made possible the expansion of charity and philanthropy which helped to mitigate failure and misfortune.

SEVEN

People and Systems

SOONER OR later everyone gets involved, either actively or passively, in one or more system. Born into a social system; brought up under an education system; behaviour and attitudes probably influenced by some religious or ideological system; governed by political and judicial systems and trying to make a living in an economic system – that is if various degrees of chaos can be described as economic systems. In fact it is difficult to imagine any human group or community, however primitive or sophisticated, surviving, let alone flourishing, without a framework of systems.

Such systems come in one of two forms. They are either the consequence of natural evolution or they are the product of a personal theory. Evolved systems are more likely to be found in groups or communities with a broadly democratic nature, while the theoretical systems are the result of, or are used to justify, an authoritarian régime. The British Common Law and Parliamentary systems are the product of natural evolution, whereas the Napoleonic legal code is the creation of an individual and Marxist régimes are the result of an individual theory. It is strange that the word 'democratic' appears so often in the titles of patently authoritarian systems, whereas the naturally democratic systems see no need to use the word in this way.

I think it might be reasonable to suppose that the basic systems – social, military, religious, administrative, legal and political – had their origins in response to experience of chaos and anarchy and the evident need to regulate activities and relationships in such a way as to ensure the survival of the community.

The fact that the organisation of armies has hardly changed since the time of Darius and Alexander the Great suggests that, where the consequences of success and failure in war can be so important, there is such a thing as an optimum military system. Armies and their leaders can be inspired by different ideologies but when it comes to doing battle the tendency has always been to adopt the system known to offer the best chance of success.

The most remarkable feature of the successful military systems is that they are capable of persuading men to risk their lives, frequently for purposes, however worthy, that can have little direct interest to the individual soldiers. This is in remarkable contrast to the industrial system where people so often appear to be ready to destroy the very organisation that provides them with a living.

Religions are perhaps not most aptly described as systems and yet the fact remains that the methods adopted by the various religions to give effect to their beliefs, and in order to influence their adherents, have much in common.

The differences depend on whether their founders or their leaders see their purpose as influencing the spiritual development of individuals or as organising a comprehensive system of behaviour for the whole community. In the first case the religion exerts its influence on individual behaviour within the social, military, legal and political systems, and is thus complementary to them. In the latter case all the other systems are incorporated into the dominant religious system.

The weakness of all systems is that human nature so easily succumbs to temptation. Religions are no exception. Indeed, the reformation of the Roman Christian Church could be said to be the direct consequence of so many of its leaders failing to resist the temptations of the seven deadly sins. Such malpractices have appeared in one form or another at one time or another among the members of all religious systems. If religious systems have a particular weakness of their own it is probably the magnification of zeal, from which follows intolerance, animosity and community strife. However, this must be set against their remarkable success in stimulating civilised and compassionate behaviour among the majority of their members.

Magnification of zeal is not peculiar to religious groups. Some people seem to have an obsession for joining organisations, and apparently the more violent and vociferous the better. Not much separates the chanting of the Nazi zealots from the chanting of the so-called protest groups; storm-troopers from terrorists; or nationalists from jingoists. Righteous zeal corrupts them all equally with equally disastrous consequences.

Civil administration is complementary to political legislation and, in theory at least, its purpose is to put into effect the decisions of the executive. However, like all systems, it tends to develop a life of its own and, human nature being what it is, the people in the system are inclined to respond to the pressures and temptations peculiar to their circumstances, just like anyone else. In very crude and simplified terms, the criterion for success and advancement in any administrative system tends to be the avoidance of mistakes rather than the exercise of initiative.

Furthermore, as is not the case with commerce, there is little or no direct reward for the efficient application of the very considerable economic resources for which the civil administration is responsible. One of the perennial problems of all Governments is the control of public expenditure, and since it became fashionable for Governments to make themselves responsible for more and more activities within the state, the problem of the control of this expenditure has become correspondingly intractable.

Judicial and legal systems suffer in much the same way. Philosophers have had no great difficulty in defining the concepts of perfect justice nor in devising more or less rational systems for administering it. The trouble is that even legal systems are liable to be corrupted by the ordinary human weaknesses of some judges and lawyers. But, more significantly, there are many instances where judgement is influenced by religious or social systems, or where the whole legal procedure comes under the much more severe pressure of authoritarian political systems. The famous 'show trials' of the Stalin era in the Soviet Union offer probably the most glaring example.

In naturally evolving systems their character is likely to be derived from the nature of the members of the community and from the practical circumstances in which they are trying to survive. History seems to suggest that the most successful communities or nations in terms of military success or cultural development are those where the basic systems are in reasonable balance with one another and mutually compatible. The early days of the Roman Empire and the departure of the Jews from Egypt and the successful settlement of the Promised Land are examples of such a balanced situation although the leadership of one was military and the other religious.

The process of natural evolution in systems depends on the fact that human behaviour is controlled by a combination of rational analysis and irrational emotion. For example, logic dictates that everyone should be treated fairly and equally, hence laws and customs applicable to all. But emotion demands a certain amount of individual freedom of action and, as individuals act differently and have different ambitions, such freedom inevitably causes inequalities. In fact freedom is seldom comparable with equality. Furthermore, the control or enforcement of a fair and equal system involves some sort of administrative hierarchy which itself entails an unequal distribution of power, responsibility and rewards. Even in tribal systems, which are probably the nearest to egalitarian, there are chiefs, priests and witch-doctors enjoying special status. The great argument between Lenin and Trotsky was due, at least in part, to the fact that Lenin could see that state control could only be exercised by a state bureaucracy, whereas Trotsky could see that such a bureaucracy would effectively prevent the achievement of the Marxist ideal of communism without government.

The feature of an evolving system, such as a Parliamentary democracy, or a religion without a comprehensive text book such as Hinduism, is that it functions by general consent. It is true that the philosophy of a particular party or faction may dominate it for a while, but provided the dominant group does not destroy the fundamental process by which consensus is achieved, the pendulum of public opinion will usually swing back from any excess. The essential point is that the best intentions do not justify the destruction of basic liberties, or coercion in any form. The ambition to achieve a fair and honest system by consent is infinitely preferable to the conviction that there is only one divinely or intellectually inspired solution to all the complex problems of human communities.

It is interesting that Marx, who was largely responsible for one of the utopian egalitarian systems, did not really object to the wildly unequal feudal system, because he maintained that under it everyone had their rights and responsibilities. It was, in his view, the irresponsible exercise of power and private wealth by the bourgeois capitalists that caused all the trouble. Unfortunately his solution has proved to be worse than the original problem.

In contrast to the naturally evolving systems are those created by deliberate design. These are usually based on some intellectual assessment of what is best for the community or on the desire to achieve the intentions of the designer. These might be described as utopian systems and, since their inventors usually refuse to accept that there is such a thing as human nature, such systems inevitably degenerate into some form of more or less oppressive dictatorship. The common denominator of all dictatorships is the suppression of the influence of any dissenting group or individuals on the operation of the system. The natural reaction is for the victims of such oppression to attempt to get away. There are no refugees from free and democratic systems, but even dictatorships established with the best possible intention need walls and curtains to prevent their citizens from voting with their feet.

There are socio-economic systems such as those based on Marxism, and there are benevolent theocratic dictatorship systems, of which the Inca régime in South America is probably the most extreme example. In modern days there are a number of states which have been declared to be Islamic where the rules laid down in the Koran are strictly applied in law, politics and society as a whole as well as in religious observance. Military dictatorships are usually a consequence of an actual or threatened period of anarchy following a breakdown in ordinary civil government. In a state of chaos the man with the gun has the last word.

Authoritarian systems are not invariably the product of utopian ideas. They are just as likely to derive from the ambition of one man, with the help of a gang or family, for power. There is, incidentally, a popular misconception that power is achieved by wealth, whereas the exact opposite is much more likely to be the case, unless of course there is so much corruption that money can buy influence over the system or at least purchase immunity from its control. There are also many cases, such as Chile, where the overthrow of an intolerant ideological system has merely produced an equally undesirable authoritarian system in its place, but with a different political philosophy. Hitler and Mussolini's régimes were based on anti-communism, although what is now known as fascism was the consequence. De Gaulle was also convinced of the dangers of extreme socialism but in his case his faith in the free democratic principle was strong enough to overcome any personal ambition for permanent absolute power.

Utopians frequently claim that all social ills can be cured quite simply by more education. Unfortunately the statistics do not bear this out. A higher proportion of the population now spends longer at school and in further education than at any time in British history. Yet the figures for juvenile and adult crime are also at their highest levels ever. If the education system is to cure social ills then scholarship and intellectual ability alone are not sufficient objectives. Moral values and social respon-sibilities are even more important in the development of civilised individuals. If the claim that education can be responsible for the cure of social ills is to be credible, the education system must accept the same share of responsibility if it fails to justify its claims.

A process of self-correction through the democratic structure is a normal part of the evolving systems. On the other hand, states which get taken over by political ideologies experience all the stresses and strains of a rigid and inflexible imposed system of supposed equality, not much evident fraternity, practically no liberty, and become heavily dependent on the more prosperous economies for technological and financial resources. The irony of it is that the present-day successors to the intellectuals who devised and introduced these supposedly utopian egalitarian systems are their most vocal dissidents. While the majority of the people living under whichever system either tacitly supports or grudgingly tolerates the whole spectrum of particular systems, quite a large proportion of the community is gainfully employed in running or administering one or other of the particular systems. Human nature being what it is, the chances are that they will attempt to manipulate their system to their own advantage. Paradoxically it is usually the exploiters of one system who wax most indignant when they find that their fellow citizens are doing the same thing in other systems. At the other extreme are the anarchists who are against all systems on principle, though experience suggests that a non-system very soon gets taken over by the most ruthless and dedicated gang. The vacuum created by the weakness of the Weimar Republic was quickly filled by Hitler's storm-troopers.

As it is virtually impossible for an imposed system based on a text book to evolve in the normal way, any change presumably has to come about as a result of another revolution. However, it so happens that such a large proportion of the people is employed in running and administering the imposed system that, no matter what individuals may think of it in theory, it provides a great many of them with a living in practice. Furthermore, in an oppressive system the oppressors enjoy considerable advantages and the devil you know is usually more acceptable than trusting in the theoretical possibility of being as well off under a more angelic system. Successful counter-revolutions depend just as much on the support of those who hope to be better off under a different system as on those who want to get rid of the old system.

The difficulty of the utopian systems is that they lack the essential flexibility to allow for changes in public attitudes and outlook. Marxism, for instance, or the temporal aspects of Islam, are constrained by the teachings of their founders whether all of them have a contemporary relevance or not. Cynical disregard for inconvenient aspects of the teaching ends up by reinforcing the power of the self-appointed authorities as it leaves them free to make up the rules to suit themselves as they go along.

Even evolved systems can achieve an imbalance in social advantages and disadvantages. The caste system in India was not conceived by some social ideologist, it simply evolved and by degrees it achieved the standing of immutable law. It never had the force of law but it became so entrenched in custom that even when attitudes have changed it still proves very difficult to eradicate it entirely.

The fact is that no system can of itself guarantee a successful community. Even the most carefully thought out or highly refined system needs a consensus support if it is to work effectively. People must believe in it – warts and all. As Winston Churchill said, parliamentary democracy is a bad system of government; its only merit is that it is better than any other system, but even then of course everyone must be agreed in wanting it to work and in trying to make it work as equitably as possible.

Without such belief the system becomes corrupted. It either comes to be used cynically for personal advantage without thought for the common good, which was its original purpose; or it fails because it turns out to be incompatible with the ordinary rules of human nature. All systems, religious, political, legal, military, education, economic, and many others, can become corrupted in this way and, like one rotten apple in the barrel, it is liable to infect all the others.

The important thing to remember is that this corruption, this infection, takes shape in people's minds, it does not have to be the direct product of the system. For example, it is not very difficult to corrupt, for whatever reason, a smoothly running education system in such a way that when the corrupted minds find their way into other perfectly healthy systems they will begin to rot them from within.

Probably the most glaring examples of the corruption of systems by the least attractive qualities and instincts of human nature can be found in some of the world's great religions. Almost without exception they preach peace, goodwill and the brotherhood of man, and yet many of them have been used by the unscrupulous to cause more human conflict and misery than any other system, save perhaps communism.

The most intractable problem for even the best intentioned systems occurs when people acquire a vested interest in keeping them as they are.

The conflict then arises between those who patently, and possibly unfairly, benefit from the system and those who feel that they are disadvantaged or victims of the system and consequently become opponents, dissidents or defectors. Such opponents are easily totally committed to the overthrow of the system as a whole so that even quite radical concessions become unacceptable.

The conventional view is that opposition to a system is primarily generated by envy of the power and wealth enjoyed by those who control it. This may be a part but it is not the whole reason. But, since wealth is more likely to be derived from power than the other way round, the temptation to acquire power is twofold. Power is attractive for its own sake, but it is made that much more attractive by the prospect of using it in order to acquire wealth. Once a combination of wealth and power has been achieved the temptation to take advantage of it to avoid the normal control and processes of law, or to deny the redress of grievances to those without power, becomes overwhelming.

It is this immunity from the law together with the power to introduce and to enforce oppressive laws on the rest of the community that creates the social imbalance and causes the greatest indignation. Envy and jealousy of power and wealth are only natural but, if it can be seen that they were legitimately acquired and responsibly used, there is little evidence to show that they have on their own caused any major social upheavals.

Unfair treatment, discrimination, corruption and perversion of justice have always caused the deepest anger and resentment. Human nature has seen to it that every system has suffered from social imbalance in one form or another at some period or other. The chances of correcting such imbalance are much greater in a free society than under a rigidly imposed egalitarian system.

Of course, all systems can fail for other reasons. Even demonstrably good systems will fail if they are incompetently administered. Equally, super-efficient angels cannot make a bad system work. The great risk of the intellectually conceived systems is that, while they may be devised with the best possible intentions and satisfy the rational and analytical faculties of their authors, they are more than likely to frustrate the natural hopes and aspirations of the very people for whom they were devised, no matter how efficiently they are administered. Even in a Parliamentary system individual pieces of legislation have been known to have exactly the opposite effect to that intended by their authors. If such legislation is a consequence of an empirical effort to solve a problem it should be possible to correct it if the need arises, but if it derives from political dogma it becomes almost impossible to shift.

EIGHT

Subsidies, Price Controls and Grants

THE APPARENTLY obvious solution to a problem is seldom, if ever, the right solution. One very good reason for this is that problems are never as straightforward as they appear to be at first sight. Furthermore, in the real world, neither the problems nor their solutions bear any obvious relationship to what the theorists and ideologists believe them to be. This may well be due to the fact that ideologies create problems where none exist and that theoretical solutions are largely based on good intentions. Unfortunately experience shows that good intentions are not the same thing as good solutions. For instance, the obvious solution to the problem of cracking a nut may be to hit it with a sledgehammer. The intention is undoubtedly good, but the solution is demonstrably bad.

It may seem to be a glimpse of the obvious, but the clue to finding a proper solution is to study the problem and to identify exactly what needs to be solved. To go back to the nut. A little reflection will reveal that the problem is not how to crack the nut, but to find a way of extracting the kernel with as little damage as possible. Once this has been established the sledgehammer solution is obviously the wrong one.

An example of a different sort of misapprehension of a problem is the offer of bounties for the killing and eradication of certain pests. The system has been tried with rabbits and grey squirrels. The difficulty is that offering a bounty for killing is no different from offering a price for producing. Consequently, instead of achieving eradication of the pest, bounties are an encouragement to 'farm' it as a regular source of income.

The most persistent and universal problem is that of human poverty and the discovery of its solution. Merely putting the blame on to another group in society or on to some system or other has never come near to finding a solution. The fact is that every society in history has tried, without conspicuous success, to cope with the problem of poverty. Some people for whatever reason or through no fault of their own are incapable of making ends meet. The most obvious solution is to do away with the need of the poor to pay the full cost of the goods and services they require, and the most obvious means to achieve this is for the Government to pay for the services out of taxes. The State School education system and the National Health Service are examples of services provided at no direct cost to the consumer and consequently freely available to those who cannot afford them. So far so good, but these subsidies benefit all consumers, rich and poor equally, consequently they are very expensive and offer no relative advantage to the poor.

In housing, the situation is slightly different. Subsidised houses are intended for the poor or, to be more accurate, they are intended for people who are poor at the time they apply for a house. Presumably the assumption is that the 'group of poor' in a society is permanently composed of the same individuals. 'Tied' or rent-free accommodation was never intended to benefit the poor in particular. In present-day jargon it would be described as a fringe benefit.

Of course it may be entirely a coincidence that there has been a more or less severe housing problem in Britain since the war whereas in Germany, which started with a much smaller stock, housing ceased to be a problem many years ago. The essential difference is that the British system subsidises the houses, whoever occupies them, whereas the German system subsidises the needy inhabitants.

Food being even more vitally important than housing, the solutions to the problem of making it possible for the poor to acquire the food they need are even more numerous and varied. But the difficulty about food is that so much of the raw material for conversion to edible food is produced by people who are themselves poor. Consequently subsidies intended to keep prices up for producers have to be counteracted by subsidies to keep prices down for consumers. This causes a whole string of consequential difficulties particularly because the problems of the two groups are completely different.

For one thing the consumer is only interested in the price he has to pay for food, whereas the producer is concerned about the price he can get for his agricultural products. The situation is further confounded by food aid offered by the more affluent countries to countries unable themselves to produce sufficient food for their inhabitants.

With the laudable intention of keeping the price of bread, for instance, within the reach of the poor, many Governments 'control' the price of bread. Here again the solution misses the point. Since the subsidy is applied to the commodity it benefits all consumers equally and therefore gives the poor no relative advantage, which was presumably the original intention. But it also reacts on the producer of wheat because the price of bread no longer covers the cost of growing wheat and making the bread. This means that the Government has to subsidise the grower and the baker as well as their product and as this means raising even more taxes the Government starts looking around for cheaper supplies from the world markets or even for gifts of wheat from the more affluent countries.

The inevitable consequence is that, as they can no longer produce and sell their wheat at a profit, the home producers are either put out of business altogether and join the ranks of the poor, or they switch their production to some other more profitable crop, which may well not be food at all.

All along, the intentions have been admirable, but the failure to identify the problem properly has merely resulted in making matters worse.

It should be fairly evident that there are two problems, poor consumers and poor producers, and they need separate solutions. In order to give the poor consumer a relative advantage he needs to be given either a sum of money or a voucher, or some other form of income supplement to allow him to buy food at the market price. Selecting the recipients should present no particular problem in this country as a system of Supplementary Benefits is already in existence.

In order to give the poor producer a relative advantage, compared to the bigger and more efficient competitor, he needs to have the costs of production subsidised either by a higher price for his product or by lower prices for his inputs; that is seeds, fertilisers, chemicals, fuel, machinery, transport and so on. True, this is applying a subsidy to a commodity, but the essential point is to ensure that the subsidy only goes to those who are deemed to need it.

Since farmers already claim back the VAT paid on the purchase of their inputs it should be possible to devise a scheme of bonuses based on claims for repayment of VAT so that smaller purchases attract bigger bonuses. The scale of bonuses would diminish as the purchases got bigger until they faded out at some median level.

An alternative or additional scheme of subsidised seasonal or short-term credit finance for small farmers through artificially low interest rates, and also based on claims for repayment of VAT, should not be too complicated to work.

The point about food aid is that it is intended to make up the deficiency in food production in the receiving country and not as a free gift to the consumer. Consequently, if it is not to put the small producer out of business, the proper recipient of the gift food should be the food producer who can then sell it, together with his own production, thus providing him with an increased income and the consumer with an increased supply of food.

It may well be that the troubles of the EEC's Common Agricultural Policy have their origin in the failure to identify these problems correctly in the first place. Just because food is common to producers and consumers does not mean that it poses the same problems to both. Yet the interests of both are supposed to be the responsibility of the same authority. Furthermore, by subsidising the prices paid to all producers and the prices paid by all consumers, rather than the needy individuals, a whole new series of problems have been created.

If, as seems likely, one of the intentions of the CAP is to benefit the small and relatively disadvantaged producer by putting a price on his product that will keep him in business, the inevitable consequence is that the bigger, and probably more efficient, producer will cash in on this bonanza; the result is massive over-production at a very great cost to the taxpayer. Incidentally, it also creates an awkward problem for the authority in disposing of these unwanted stocks.

This sort of thing would happen with any form of industrial production but agriculture is very much more complicated. Workshops and factories are alike the world over, but agricultural production depends on soil type, climate, rainfall, geographical location and systems of land tenure, social traditions and a host of other variables. The farmers in the Welsh valleys and hills or in the Scottish highlands have a different set of criteria from the farmers in East Anglia. Yet such things as the subsidy on fertilisers, for example, apply equally to all farmers. The requirement to apply subsidies to the people who most need them is therefore even more important in agriculture.

The traditional way of transferring the products of the producer to the consumer is through a market. This applies in food although only a very small proportion goes directly from producer to consumer. Much the greater proportion of agricultural production is only the raw material for the food processors, and a sizeable part of it, such as tobacco, sisal and cotton, does not go into food at all. The agricultural producer is therefore dealing with commodity markets, rather than consumer markets, and with all the fluctuations for which these markets are renowned.

Since the farmer's inputs are more or less fixed, such price fluctuations, together with fluctuations in volume of output due to climatic variation, cause serious difficulties. Furthermore, the volume of output is closely related to the anticipated price.

In order to overcome the difficulties created by such fluctuations and to influence the volume of output of particular commodities, Governments and producer organisations introduce price-fixing mechanisms or marketing boards. Price level is not the sole criterion for the volume of production, but it has a very important influence. For example, in 1980 the Government of Zimbabwe, amongst other measures to help small farmers, increased the price paid for maize by about 40 per cent and within two years the delivery of maize from small farmers increased by 500 per cent.

The traditional, and effective, method of smoothing out these inevitable fluctuations is for a producer's, or a Government, agency to buy stocks when the price is low, and thus keeping the price up, or by selling stocks when prices are climbing so as to prevent the price going too high.

A favourite way of trying to influence agricultural producers is to offer grants for particular purposes that are deemed to be important. However, such a system does not always produce the desired result. For instance, in an attempt to increase agricultural output, farmers in hill areas were offered grants for ploughing up previously uncultivated land. Needless to say there was no lack of applicants but in many instances once the grant was received nothing was planted.

One of the very obvious weaknesses of the whole grants system is that they are frequently offered by different agencies for diametrically opposite purposes. Grants intended to encourage 'development', such as drainage and hedge-cutting schemes, have an exactly opposite effect to grants offered for 'conservation' purposes.

In some cases grants, which are simply a different form of subsidy, are offered for capital projects such as new buildings. Since the grant is on a certain proportion of the cost of the project, the system inevitably works to the advantage of the larger farmer. Taxation, through allowances for certain purposes before tax is assessed, is yet another method for applying subsidies, but here again the tendency is to favour the more successful farmer as the poorer farmer is anyway less likely to have a taxable surplus.

The inevitable conclusion is that the whole structure of subsidies, particularly for agriculture, is needlessly complicated and in many cases counter-productive. I do not think it would be unreasonable to suggest that in principle measures intended to subsidise the consumers of food should be completely separated from measures intended to subsidise agricultural producers. Further, that food aid should be seen as a contribution to a deficiency in production and not as a contribution to consumption. In any event, aid to produce food is far more effective than food aid.

The evidence also suggests that in principle it is better to subsidise the person than the commodity; that subsidies intended to keep down the price of food equally to all consumers is a waste of time and money, and that subsidies intended to give advantages to all producers equally not only fail to achieve the intention of helping the needy, they create quite unnecessary problems in the disposal of the resulting surplus.

A completely free market system cannot give an advantage to the small producer or to the poor consumer, but subsidies applied in the wrong way are no improvement.

PART II

Science and Natural History

ONE

The March of Science

IN A REVIEW of British science and technology 1851 is a convenient starting point for two reasons. Firstly, the Exhibition of that year can be regarded as a gigantic stocktaking of the national resources and technical skill. Secondly, because it marked the end of the Industrial Revolution and the conversion of Victorian England to the policy of industrial expansion on which our future still depends. The period as a whole saw the climax of our industrial supremacy and its inevitable decline when countries with greater resources and population learned from us the lessons of the mechanisation of industry. It also covers the birth and growth of the new concepts of modern science.

Social conditions in the middle of the last century were, generally speaking, the outcome of the Industrial Revolution, but with all the traditions of the England of agriculture, cottage industry and small market towns. The population of twenty millions was growing fast but still small compared to our fifty millions of today. Education was limited to a minority and was almost entirely classical, so the new profession of engineering had to draw its recruits from a different sphere, that of self-educated men. A new wealthy class was growing up in the commercial world to rival the old aristocracy. There was unbounded optimism about the future and ample scope in commerce and industry to attract all intelligent and enterprising men. The number of poor was on the increase and their conditions were deteriorating because, as yet, no social conscience had grown up to replace the patriarchal responsibility of the landowners and master craftsmen.

In the domestic field, lighting was by candle and oil lamps, cooking and heating by coal or wood in ranges or open fires with the consequent enormous waste of energy. Food had to be fresh or crudely preserved, and thus needed to be produced locally. In health and hygiene the figures speak for themselves. In 1851 the infant death rate was 150 per 1,000 living births compared with 25 per 1,000 today. Anaesthetics, antiseptic surgery, biochemistry, tropical medicine, were all virtually unknown or in their infancy. Psychology had not yet achieved independence from philosophy on the one hand and physiology on the other.

This was the age of the practical engineer and of processes arrived at by intuition born of experience and by trial and error. Technology was concerned with the application of steam power, with metallurgy and the working of metals for various purposes, and with the production of machine tools and precision machinery. Men were already turning their minds to other types of engines and the internal combustion engine was in the process of development.

Scientists, while continuing their search for the secrets of nature, were beginning to turn their attention to exploring the empirical developments of industry. Their numbers as yet were small, the endowments for research were negligible and much of their work was carried out in the watertight compartments of the different sciences. But the seed had been sown and it was not long before scientists and engineers were preparing the way for the great technological harvest of the twentieth century.

The changes brought about in the lives of men and women in the last hundred years have been greater and more rapid than during any other period in history, and these changes have been almost entirely due to the work of scientists and technologists all over the world. They have not only affected the way of living of all civilised peoples but have also vastly increased our knowledge about ourselves, the earth we live on and the universe around us. I cannot emphasise too much that the sum total of scientific knowledge and technological progress is an international achievement to which every civilised country has made some contribution.

And now, before considering the contribution of the British Commonwealth, I should like to sketch what appear to a layman like myself to have been the main influences on the course of scientific and technical achievement since 1851 and their relation to one another.

The great stimulus of the 1851 Exhibition created a growing interest in technical education and research, followed by a widening of the scientific horizon which was soon to find expression in borderline subjects. For the next fifty years science advanced rapidly, but in most fields there was a wide gap between science and industry. Electricity was an exception and the groundwork was already being laid for the electrical revolution of the Victorian age. Medicine was on the verge of breaking away from mediaeval practice and taking the first steps towards its modern pattern, while

British colonial development stimulated the study of tropical disease.

Between 1851 and 1870 practice, in many industries, was ahead of science, and in that period the large number of inventions of the Industrial Revolution were progressively improved and widely applied. These inventions, which added so much to our industrial production, were mainly the work of British genius. They were of great economic advantage to this country and were quickly exploited commercially. New factories and plants were built to include the very latest ideas, and with the expansion of industry came the demand for more and more new ideas and greater efficiency. This demand was a direct stimulus to technological invention as well as an indirect stimulus to science. We are still struggling with the social results of this vast expansion.

From 1870 to 1890 the highwater mark of British industrial expansion, as compared with other countries, had been reached and the competition of the United States and Europe was just beginning to be felt. But the lack of serious competition hitherto had bred a feeling of over-confidence and satisfaction in the methods and processes employed. The result was a conservative attitude towards technical change and, particularly in the older industries, neglect of scientific research. Accumulation of wealth and the income from foreign investments in any case made the country as a whole less dependent on the efficiency of her industries. Concurrently a subtle change occurred in the type of British exports. So far the products of our machinery, such as rails and rolling stock, had been shipped abroad for immediate use, but now machines themselves were exported to do their work in the factories of Europe and America instead of in Britain. The result of this was to intensify foreign industrial competition between 1890 and 1914, but with the increasing demands from the Colonies the volume of British exports was not greatly affected.

Then came the critical years of the First World War bringing a realisation of the part science must play in the industrial and military strength of the nation. For the first time in history a real attempt was made to enlist the services of science in the war effort and the Department of Scientific and Industrial Research was founded to further the application of science in industry through Government Laboratories and Research Associations.

The effects of these measures appeared clearly in the inter-war years when there was a marked swing of education from classics towards science. Coupled with this the war had directed the attention of many research scientists to practical objectives, so that after the war there was a rapid expansion of industrial research. Scientific progress was no longer confined to the work of a few brilliant individuals, but came also from teams of research scientists each working on different parts of the same problem. It was during this period that many new commercial research laboratories grew up, employing scientists to discover new processes and materials connected with their industry as a direct weapon of competition.

The war had also shown a great weakness in our dependence on foreign production for many vital articles, such as dyestuffs, scientific instruments and optical glass, in the manufacture of which scientific research played an essential part. This weakness was remedied with the help of the Key Industry Import Duties which gave the necessary support and encouragement to the establishment of these industries at home.

It is true that manufacturers in some of the older industries still clung to traditional methods in spite of the pressure of competition from America and other countries. And in this connection it is significant that the history of production engineering after 1890 is almost entirely confined to the United States.

It was however a period of rapid development in Britain. The invention of the internal combustion engine and the pneumatic tyre had opened new branches of industrial engineering, and the demand for fuel for motor cars and aircraft gave birth to the new technology of oil. In the electrical, chemical and aircraft industries, science was fully enlisted in the fields of electronics, synthetic fibres, plastics, aerodynamics and light alloys. Consequently the outbreak of war in 1939 found us in a much stronger position to meet the immense demands it made on all branches of technology for new gadgets, machines and weapons. From the outset science in all its forms and branches was harnessed and completely co-ordinated with the war effort. It was only the intimate partnership of science and engineering with the Staffs of the Fighting Services that enabled us to meet swiftly and effectively the ever-changing menace of total war.

The tremendous demands on our industries had some good after-effects. Once again these demands revealed weaknesses where our industrial capacity was out of date. The realisation of this has initiated comprehensive reconstruction on most modern lines. The almost complete absence of income from our foreign investments has forced us to rely once more on our capacity to make the goods the world requires. Our industry and productivity have shown a wonderful improvement, but there is still a lot more that can be done. The rate at which scientific knowledge is being applied in many industries is too small and too slow. Our physical resources have dwindled, but the intellectual capacity of our scientists and engineers is as great as ever and it is upon their ingenuity that our future prosperity largely depends.

I would now like to make a brief survey of the British contribution to natural knowledge and technology and pay a tribute to some of the great men of science of the last hundred years.

In some branches almost the whole story can be told since one problem after another has been solved by British scientists. In others there are many blanks and gaps where the vital links in the chain were forged abroad. But looking at the whole vast field of abstract and practical science there can be no doubt that during this period the contribution of the British Commonwealth has been of outstanding importance.

Our knowledge of the stars, the heavens, and our place in the universe has increased steadily through the centuries, but since 1851 some of the most important links were supplied by such men as Eddington, Jeans and Milne in their work on mass, luminosity and stellar evolution. Huggins made a great contribution with his application of spectrum analysis to astronomy, and Lockyer's discovery of helium in the sun had a significance far beyond the realms of astrophysics.

Coming nearer to the earth, the work of Abercromby and Shaw on the behaviour of the earth's atmosphere in the troposphere started the scientific study of weather and weather prediction, and Appleton's research into the ionosphere extended this to the upper air.

Chemistry has fascinated man from the earliest times, and vast progress has been made in the last hundred years both in knowledge and theory. Much fresh ground was broken by Crookes by his work on spectra, his discovery of thallium and of 'radiant matter' known later as cathode rays. Long after everyone was quite sure of the composition of the air, Rayleigh found another ingredient which he called argon and so started the hunt for other inert gases. In organic chemistry both Perkin and Robinson have added enormously to our knowledge of the structure of carbon compounds, and to our power to copy natural products synthetically. The development of X-ray analysis by the two Braggs, father and son, has given us a means of finding the actual arrangement of the atoms in the molecule and has revealed the accuracy of the chemists' conclusions about the architecture of molecules based on their reactions with one another. This is a most striking example of the power of the theoretical and practical scientist to penetrate nature's secrets.

Going beyond the chemist and his molecules we come to the physicist and the study of even smaller particles. Thomson's discovery of the nature of the electron was the first attack upon the integrity of the atom. Next, thanks to Rutherford's brilliant research and keen intuition, came the nuclear theory which revolutionised our ideas of matter. To prove it, he was the first man to succeed in the transmutation of an element. It is appropriate to mention Moseley's work on the X-ray spectra of the elements, as it already showed such great promise, before he was killed at Gallipoli.

Parallel with this activity in the physical sciences there occurred a technological revolution of even greater scope and variety. The Darbys of Coalbrookdale were the lineal ancestors of Bessemer, Thomas and Siemens, and the whole technology of metals. First cheap cast iron followed by cheap steel, then steel from phosphatic ores, completely changed the materials available to engineers, shipbuilders and architects. Scientific metallurgy can be said to have started when Sorby first applied a microscope to the surface of metals. The way was opened for the investigation of the metallic alloys which came in quick succession from developments in which Hadfield and Rosenhain made outstanding contributions.

It was not long before the possibilities of these new materials were recognised, and the great majority of the mechanical developments of the period were due to new alloys which could withstand higher stresses. But before these materials could be fully used Maudsley and Whitworth had to lay the foundations of production engineering, and Mushet had to do pioneer work in developing tungsten steel as the first high-speed cutting tool.

The reciprocating steam engine of the Industrial Revolution was the main source of power until Parsons invented the steam turbine, which revolutionised large-scale power production on land and sea. But that was not the only source of power to rival the push-and-pull engine. The internal combustion engine, in which Dugald Clerk and Ackroyd-Stuart were among the early pioneers, has proved to be a formidable challenge in many fields. In marine engineering, Froude's work on hull forms and propellers enabled the full benefit of the new prime movers to be reaped at sea.

Here I wish I could mention early British pioneers of motor-vehicles but, as is well known, restrictive legislation drove the development of the motor-car abroad, until the repeal of the speed limit in 1903 gave scope to the genius of Royce, Lanchester and Ricardo. In place of the motor car, however, we have Lawson to thank for the invention of the safety bicycle; and all wheeled vehicles, except those running on rails, owe their rapid development to Dunlop's invention of the pneumatic tyre. The material required for this started the vast natural and synthetic rubber industry, and has made famous the name of Wickham for a brilliant feat of smuggling, when he brought the rubber seeds from Brazil to Kew, from which sprang the rubber plantation industry of the east.

In flying, the names of the pioneers and their feats are legion, and more than in any other mechanical science the development of aerodynamics has been shared by many nations, but Lanchester's vortex theory was one of the stepping stones to powered flight, and the achievement of Alcock and Brown in making the first Atlantic flight in 1919 speaks highly for the tremendous scientific and technological background of flying in this country. Of outstanding importance and consequence was the genius which Mitchell brought to aircraft design, and, more recently, Whittle's pioneer work has given us the lead in jet engine production both for civil and military use.

Following on the immense progress in metallurgy and mechanical engineering, the most far-reaching development of the period has been that of electricity and electronics. Although the key discovery belongs to Faraday in an earlier period, the second founder of the science is undoubtedly Clerk Maxwell, with his classic treatise on electro-magnetism. The use of electricity for domestic and industrial purposes was helped by Wilde's development of the dynamo and then by Swan's incandescent lamps. Wheatstone and Kelvin pioneered the use of electricity for communication by their work on line and cable telegraphy. Wireless telegraph soon followed and the work on tuned circuits by Lodge, and Marconi's many brilliant developments made in this country with the General Post Office and the Navy, soon made radio a practical proposition. Heaviside and Appleton made further contributions on the propagation of radio waves. It is interesting to see that the technique used by Appleton in his pulse-ranging on the ionosphere and upper layers was later developed by Watson-Watt into radar which is now almost indispensable to airmen and seamen all over the world. And here Randall's development of the magnetron for high frequency radar was one of the major contributions to the Allies' equipment for war.

Television has a wide parentage, but Baird's name will always be linked with the first successful pictures.

Another great innovation of this hundred years was the discovery and development of plastic and synthetic materials. The story starts with Parke's discovery of celluloid and Cross and Bevan's manufacture of viscose which gave birth to the rayon industry and the many later types of synthetic fibre. Perkin's mauve, first of the aniline dyes and Kipping's new silicon compounds were, however, disregarded by industry in this country. But we see today a change of heart in the development in our industrial laboratories of two new plastics, perspex and polythene, with almost an unlimited range of applications in the air, on the ground, and at sea.

The effect all this has had upon the citizen varies naturally with where and how he lives, but basically it has given him reliable light and heat in his home, push-button communication with almost any part of the world and home entertainment of a high quality. His transport on land, at sea, and in the air is quick, comfortable and clean. In addition he has a vast range of materials with which to clothe himself and to furnish and embellish his home. Almost more important, these developments have brought about a complete change in his conditions of work.

But if the citizen has benefited, so too has Science from the great array of new techniques that have been invented, and the new tools with which the scientist and technologist can burrow, hack and worry at the growing mountain of problems to be solved.

So far I have dealt with the physical sciences. Now I would like to turn briefly to the biological and psychological sides, which after a slow beginning in this country have made increasingly rapid progress.

The whole field of biological science in this period is overshadowed by the works of Darwin presented in his *Origin of Species* and *The Descent of Man*. Nothing has done so much to widen man's thoughts as his conception of evolution as the great law controlling living things, 'that progress comes from unceasing competition, through increasing selection and rejection'.

In the basic study of living things some of the most important contributions from this country were the pioneer work of Francis Galton and William Bateson in the field of heredity, Sherrington's work on the integrative action of the nervous system, and Dale's and Adrian's contributions to our knowledge of the transmission of nervous impulses.

The science of biochemistry is relatively new and Gowland Hopkins was its founder in this country. His discovery of the significance of accessory food factors, leading up to the recognition of vitamins, started the modern science of nutrition. Other landmarks were Bayliss and Starling's recognition of the part played by hormones in the blood stream, followed by Banting and Best's isolation of insulin, and Harington's synthesis of thyroxin.

Fleming working on mould cultures discovered the antibacterial properties of penicillin and later Florey and Chain, at Oxford, found that penicillin could be extracted in a highly purified form, and used it to treat human disease.

Modern surgery can be said to have been born in Scotland with Simpson's discovery of the use of chloroform as an anaesthetic and Lister's antiseptic technique based on Pasteur's bacteriological discoveries. A further advance of the greatest value to surgery as a science was Macewen's aseptic technique which made surgery clean and safe, followed by his classic work on the brain and spinal cord.

If Lister was the father of modern surgery, then Manson was the father of tropical medicine, and it is particularly in this field that the British contribution has led the world. The discovery by Ross that malaria is carried by the anopheles mosquito and, much later, the work of Fairley in Australia on its prevention and cure have been of the greatest benefit to mankind. Bruce will always be remembered for his discovery of the part played by the deadly tsetse fly in the transmission of sleeping sickness and his work on Malta fever. Finlay, Adrian Stokes and Hindle stand high among the names linked with the study and prevention of yellow fever.

These were all vital efforts towards the prevention of sickness, but there is another aspect of medical practice in which the Commonwealth has taken a leading part – the promotion of health. It was Sir John Simon, the first Medical Officer appointed to a central authority, who made a careful statistical study of the causes of sickness, with a view to taking effective measures for the health of the community at large. Through his leadership health services have been provided in regular stages throughout the country. At first these were largely aimed at providing pure water, effective sanitation, and the abolition of slums; but since the beginning of the present century the *personal* health services, especially in the case of mothers, babies, and school children, have become national in scope and lead the world.

There are two other fields in which the biological sciences play a major part. The first is in the preservation of food and in nutrition which has had the most profound economic and social effects. The ability through freezing, drying and canning to import large quantities of food has enabled a rapidly increasing population to maintain and increase its standards of living, which would have been impossible had it been dependent on British agriculture alone. The scientific study of nutrition has made it possible to improve the health of the population and in war to feed the people with the minimum of waste.

Mort had the first freezing works in the world at Sydney, and was a pioneer in refrigeration, but success in transporting meat to Britain had to wait for the development of more reliable refrigerating plant. Since 1918 the Food Investigation Laboratories of the Department of Scientific and Industrial Research, of which Sir William Hardy was the first director, have established the basic biological knowledge on which the storage and transport of meat, fish and fruit are now largely based.

The second field is in agriculture, where in order to compete with cheap foreign foods the most successful farmer is one who enlists the full assistance of science. Lawes, who discovered how to make and use superphosphate, and started the great fertiliser industry, was quick to realise this. He founded Rothamsted, now the oldest agricultural research station in the world, and there he and Gilbert carried out the first scientifically controlled field experiments which laid the foundation of agricultural science. Later, Biffen's pioneer work in plant breeding at Cambridge became one of the greatest contributions to the problem of feeding the world's growing population. He showed how it was possible to breed strains of wheat combining resistance to disease with high yields and good milling properties. In the field of animal breeding, the foundation of the most important aspect of British agriculture today, I will mention amongst the many investigators only Cossar Ewart and Crew who did so much to advance its scientific study. The mechanisation which was to revolutionise farming in all parts of the world was also under way and Britain was playing a leading part. The reaping machine, for instance, was invented by Patrick Bell in 1826 although it was not manufactured until 1853.

There is no need to point out the effect which all these improvements, discoveries and inventions have had on Society. It is this group of biological sciences which have had the most far-reaching social results, and it is particularly during and since the last war that it has been possible to exploit them.

There is one science which I have not yet mentioned. It is both the youngest science and the oldest problem. The study of man's mind was the province of the philosopher until the middle of the nineteenth century, when it separated from him and began its independent existence as the science of psychology. The foundations were not laid in this country, but important contributions were made, both from the biological and the philosophical sides by men like Ferrier, Bain and Ward. Sully's work on child psychology was the first of its kind. But probably the most outstanding figure in this country was Galton, whose teaching is widely respected in all psychological laboratories, and who was the first to develop an interest in the mental differences between individuals – a field in which British psychology has made some of its greatest contributions. Again it is only recently that full practical advantage is being taken of the progress made in this branch of science, but the results of that application may be as important as the many more easily understood developments in the purely physical world.

The story of the British contribution to science in the past century is indeed impressive, but this story would not be complete without studying the wider implications of their work and examining some of the lessons to be learnt from it.

The concrete measurement and indirect effect of all scientific effort is the general improvement in the condition in which people live and work, it is in the improvement in health, in the expectation of life and standards of living. The latter includes not only food and clothing, but housing, home comforts, medical care, education, books and newspapers, recreations and travel facilities. In every one of these directions the progress that has been made has amounted to a revolution.

Not all this springs directly from science and invention. Much has been due to the politicians and administrators, and behind them to religion, morals, education, art and the complex influences which we call culture. But even there Science has stood beside the authors of progress to advise, to help and sometimes to guide.

Now as science and technology are so vital to the future strength and prosperity of the British Commonwealth, the great problem is to discover the conditions under which they are most likely to flourish. The records show that both depend very much on co-operation, and upon the linking up of a long chain of discoveries, one with another; so that it is quite exceptional for the credit of a great advance to belong to one man or even to one country, although it will always require a flash of inspiration to weld the links into the chain. Today the development of teamwork in laboratories has made this truer than ever. For many reasons, but principally because of the increasing complexity of research and its cost, such teamwork is becoming more and more the rule. We need not repine at this but it would be a disaster if the individual inquirer working in his own laboratory were discouraged out of existence.

While the quality of scientific work is determined by the quality of the scientist, the quantity of scientific output is determined by the money available. The rapid progress of science in Britain has owed much to the growing support and sympathy of government and individual benefactors and to the endowment of research by industrial corporations. However, the basic discoveries that mark the great advances depend on the accident of individual genius and are not at our command.

The scope and intensity of the progress of applied science and technology on the other hand bear a close relationship to the circumstances of the time. Technology, as the combination of scientific knowledge with the practical ability of the inventor to apply that knowledge to the solution of particular problems, comes into play with any new discovery of scientific fact. The latest particle of truth is then developed, according to the circumstances of the time for military, commercial or medico-social purposes. It is a sad reflection that the urgent demands of modern war can produce advances that might otherwise take many years to develop, especially in the costly and uncertain experimental stages.

The rivalry between large commercial undertakings, using science to improve their products or processes as a direct means of competition, has produced a steady flow of improvements and developments. However, the fruits of this form of scientific work are sometimes open to considerable misuse. The discoveries of these commercial laboratories may be kept secret and in some cases a number of teams may be working on the same problem, which may have already been solved elsewhere. The buying up and suppression of patents and discoveries to protect equipment from becoming obsolete has also been known to happen. I am glad to see, however, a change of outlook in the growing quantity of publication of the results of industrial research.

It would seem that science has become so well established that nothing can stand in the way of its natural growth. This is far from the truth. Since the earliest times the natural conservatism of laymen has acted as a powerful brake to the adoption of new ideas, which do not rigidly conform to his notion of the correct order of things. In its most violent form it will produce unreasoning anger and utter disbelief in face of the clearest evidence or provoke plain ordinary laughter. The storm raised by Darwin's *Origin of Species* is an excellent example where even scientists failed to keep an open mind.

The position seems better today and I am sure that Sir Harold Hartley spoke for all scientists, when he said: 'Today, with our greater understanding, there is humility in the minds of all scientists. The further we penetrate into Nature's secrets the more clearly we see the ever-receding frontiers of knowledge.'

The resistance towards anything new or unexpected is balanced on the other hand by bursts of enthusiasm that some particular discovery or invention will see the end of all our troubles. The belief in the philosopher's stone seems to be just as great as ever.

As the front of pure science has advanced so its lines of communication to practical exploitation have got longer and longer. The time was when the whole process of discovery, application and exploitation could be achieved by one man. In our time a great army of scientists, technicians, inventors, designers and production engineers are required to keep the lines of communication open. Quite how important some of the members of this follow-up team have become is not always appreciated. In 1948 Sir Henry Tizard emphasised this point when he said: 'All depends on good design and production. Our weakness in the war was not to be found in what was best to do, nor in the scientific work of how to do it. It was when the stage of design and production was reached that we fell short of the best standards.' This was true already when Whitworth invented the screw micrometer, which was subsequently put into production in Germany and the United States and up to the 1914 war all micrometers had to be imported into this country.

To Professor Kipping of Nottingham goes the credit for the basic work which led to the development of silicones in Russia and the United States and yet until this year we have been dependent on imports from America of marketable silicone products.

There are many cases in the Navy where a piece of apparatus has been used operationally exactly as the inventor put it together, with all the resulting disadvantages in maintenance and efficient operation. The limitation in performance, except in some cases, is practical as opposed to scientific. Where the basic scientific principles are known by all nations the advantage lies in the good design of equipment for practical use.

A more general and far-reaching matter for concern and possibly the most vital factor affecting the industrial application of scientific research is the lack of a co-ordinated system of scientific and technological education in this country. Excellent as they are, the existing institutions, which have grown up to meet particular circumstances, do not produce anything like enough trained technologists to meet the urgent needs of scientific development in industry and to provide leaders for the future. It is to be hoped that the new and rather uncertain science of education will develop sufficiently quickly to point the way to a speedy solution of this problem.

The shortage in Britain of 'personnel trained and eager to apply scientific knowledge and scientific methods to practical ends' – as Sir Ewart Smith put it – is only one of the many shortages which the world is now facing. Among them are food, non-ferrous metals, steel alloy metals and sulphur. These very shortages are due to the scientific complexity of present-day life and it is only by science that they can be overcome. Naturally there are many ways of tackling this problem; but the most obvious are firstly by improved design to secure economy in production and the minimum use of scarce materials. Secondly by the development of substitutes made from raw materials which are still abundant. Thirdly by the reclamation of scrap and improved methods of using low-grade ores. Finally the development of renewable raw materials such as timber to satisfy the world demand for cellulose. Some of these shortages are partly due to the huge inevitable waste of war and its consequences, and partly to the lack of any comprehensive survey of the world's resources and requirements. It is only by an accurate knowledge of the world's resources that we can foresee the scope and magnitude of the future problems that science and technology have to meet and that only they can solve.

It is, therefore, good news that the Economic and Social Council of the United Nations has resolved 'to promote the systematic survey and inventory' of those resources which are not already covered by the Food and Agriculture Organisation.

We have evolved a civilisation based on the material benefits which science and technology can provide. The present shortages are a timely reminder of the slender material foundation on which our civilisation rests and of our dependence upon science and technology.

The pursuit of truth in itself cannot produce anything evil. It is in the later stage when the facts dug up enter the process of application that the choice between the beneficent and destructive development has to be made. It is quite certain that it is an exception if any particular discovery cannot be used equally well for good and evil purposes. Happily the beneficent exploitation of scientific knowledge has kept pace with its destructive application.

In a mid-century article *The Times* put it this way: '. . . It has been an age of great achievement. The lines of progress in which the Victorians trusted have been pursued farther and faster than they foresaw. Scientific discovery, from which above all their doctrines of progress derived, has swept forward on an enormous front. The conquest of the air has made possible an intercourse and understanding between distant peoples such as our ancestors could not imagine – and it has been diverted to the vast destruction of men and cities. The invention of wireless telephony has opened a channel through which liberating truths might be proclaimed to all the listening earth – and every would-be despot has used it to suborn the blind masses into the worship of false gods. The medical art has performed miracles; the cures of immemorial pestilences have been found, infancy has been safeguarded and old age tended, so that the normal expectation of life has been extended by years – aside from the new and universal apprehension of sudden death.'

To my mind it is vital that the two sides of scientific development are fully and clearly understood, not only by the research scientist, inventor, designer and the whole scientific team, but also by all laymen. The instrument of scientific knowledge in our hands is growing more powerful every day, indeed it has reached a point when we can either set the world free from drudgery, fear, hunger and pestilence or obliterate life itself.

Progress in almost every form of human activity depends upon the continued efforts of scientists. The nation's wealth and prosperity are governed by the rapid application of science to its industries and commerce. The nation's workers depend upon science for the maintenance and improvement in their standard of health, housing and food. Finally superiority or even our ability to survive in war is a direct measure of the excellence and capacity of the scientific team.

This team of research workers and engineers has a dual responsibility, one for its work and the other as informed citizens, and it can only fulfil its proper functions if its members have a sound general education as well as a thorough training in science. It is no less important that the people who control the scientific machine, both laymen and scientists, should have a proper understanding and appreciation of what science has grown into and its place among the great forces of the world.

It is clearly our duty as citizens to see that science is used for the benefit of mankind. For, of what use is science if man does not survive?

From the Presidential Address at the
Inaugural General Meeting of the British Association
for the Advancement of Science, Edinburgh,
August 8, 1951

TWO

The Teaching of Science

THE STRUCTURE of a modern industrial society consists of a series of overlapping interdependent functional groups. Each member of these groups needs a certain amount of scientific education. For some a highly specialised scientific knowledge is essential for their work; others only need a background understanding of the scientific method and the present state of scientific knowledge.

Whatever may be the arguments about the relative merits of science and the humanities, it seems quite clear that in this day and age no one can do valuable work in any academic subject, in research, or in industry and commerce without at least some basic knowledge of science. After all, research into any subject, whether it is archaeology, history or chemistry, demands the use of the latest scientific methods and techniques. On the other hand I do not think anybody would disagree that applied science demands an understanding of social development, or that pure science can only progress with an appreciation of its historical background.

As a matter of fact I believe that the intensity of the discussion about the relative importance of science and the humanities has tended to obscure more important issues to the community at large. Outside the purely academic field the real difference in human activities lies between the group which directs the efforts of others and the group which does the purely technical work however skilful or scientific. The director of a scientific research laboratory, a business manager and a bishop have more in common with each other as administrators than they have with some specialists in their own callings.

Administration or management of some occupations needs a special degree of technical or professional knowledge, but over and above that it needs a scientific approach to management, and the use of scientific methods in administration.

I think this point is important for those engaged in science education because I believe it is sometimes overlooked that the administration of industry or of fundamental scientific research, or of education for that matter, is equally, if not more, important to the successful progress of the undertaking as the standard of actual technical work within it.

The Services are an excellent example of this and they recognise it by going to a lot of trouble to train for command in addition to technical training. Industry, of course, recognises the value of the ability to manage by higher salaries.

It is only slowly being accepted that good management requires technical knowledge as well as management knowledge, but it has always been recognised that technical knowledge and skill are essential for useful work in any trade or profession. This in turn gives rise to some very awkward problems, of which early specialisation is probably the most difficult.

There is always bound to be a very natural conflict of interest between the need to acquire the qualifications necessary for the most responsible job that a chosen career has to offer on the one hand, and the need to begin to earn a living as soon as possible on the other. Apprentices and science students are in the same boat. Boys who leave school and take a well-paid unskilled job bring home more money than the apprentice, particularly when children's allowance may cease when an apprenticeship is taken up but continues if the boy remains in school. The attraction of a good dead-end industrial research job for a science student is very tempting, particularly if the training for a responsible job takes longer and perhaps has to include some subjects which are not strictly scientific.

One point about the education and training of this group of people is that, from the unskilled labourer right through to the member of a scientific research team, advancement depends upon technical qualification, ability and experience, but not necessarily upon age. Naturally the earlier a person can gain a higher professional or technical qualification the higher up the ladder he can start, but there seems to be no absolute reason why people should not qualify for advancement at any period in their career.

The importance of this to science education is that it means that those people wishing to qualify in the scientific professions would not be limited to those at school or in the universities.

The third of the interlocking groups which I referred to earlier on include the educators themselves. Let me hasten to add that I am not implying any order of precedence by making this the third group, it was merely a matter of convenience to mention the other two first. In any case I include myself in this group. Sticking to the same vast scale of generalisation I would include in this group all those who are engaged in social duties for the benefit of the community: Medicine, education, the Church, the law and the whole range of cultural activities. The function of this group is to look after the bodily and spiritual welfare of the community, to bring intellectual comment to bear on all aspects of our civilisation, to educate, to encourage, and also to warn.

In a civilisation so entirely dominated by science and the manipulation of material resources it is quite unthinkable that anyone should seriously attempt to comment on it, to make fun of it, or to discuss it without at least some vague idea of the facts of science.

This presents an entirely different problem to science educators because the people concerned are inclined to reject the scientific attitude, either because their minds do not work that way, or because they have come to the conclusion that science and little else is responsible for all the problems of modern life. It is not really a question of whether they are right or wrong, the point is that their judgement and opinions would be immeasurably fortified by a balanced understanding of the material world around them.

Furthermore, this group may win to itself a high proportion of the genuinely creative minds, people who arrive at conclusions by instinct rather than by the tortuous and painstaking methods of the scientific worker. This ability to create need not be, and in fact seldom is, restricted to purely intellectual or cultural matters. They can contribute as much in the field of industrial and engineering design, particularly if they can be made to see the possibilities in time to acquire the necessary professional qualifications. Designers have never been able to do anything without a knowledge of their materials and the processes of manufacture.

No one would deny the importance of fundamental research in pure science, but at some point someone has to inject the beneficial findings of science into civilisation, for the sake of our material well-being, as well as to improve human behaviour. This requires a critical faculty of a very high order because there are any number of examples of the reckless and dangerous exploitation of scientific discoveries, either for commercial or other purposes.

Rachel Carson in her book *Silent Spring* made this comment: 'I contend, furthermore, that we have allowed these chemicals to be used with little or no advance investigation of their effect on soil, water, wildlife and man himself. Future generations are unlikely to condone our lack of prudent concern for the integrity of the natural world that supports all life.'

The point is that it may be scientific to do research on insecticides, but it is not scientific to use the results until all the facts are known about their direct and indirect effects. It is certainly scientific to do research on particle physics but it is nothing less than barbaric to carry out experiments which endanger the lives and health of future generations.

Scientific farming does not mean the indiscriminate use of chemicals, it means the beneficial use of all available circumstances for the good of the land, the producer and the consumer. No matter how convenient a scientific process may seem to be in industrial production, it is not scientific if it gives rise to pollution of the air or water or if it makes inhuman demands on the operators.

It is not enough for professional scientists to feel concern about these things, everybody should be able to make reasonable judgements about these matters, particularly administrators and legislators.

The mere fact that science has done so much for our civilisation should never be allowed to blind us to the dangers of science improperly used. That is why the general public attitude to science is so important.

I have included educators themselves in this group because of their power to influence the minds and attitudes of their students. The way science is presented in schools is bound to have a lasting effect on each generation.

Those who go on to practise science need a well-developed critical faculty. Potential designers in engineering and technology may be put off or drift into other spheres. Those not going into science anyway may have their whole outlook on science warped and distorted. Those who go on to be administrators may develop a suspicion of science and its methods or underestimate its impact due to an ignorance which some do not like to admit and which others like to boast about.

As it is there has been much talk about scientists leaving this country for the United States. This may be due to several causes, singly or in combination. There may be better research facilities, the demand for research scientists abroad may give rise to attractive economic inducements, there may be a more enlightened and understanding attitude towards science in general and the advantages of scientific research, or, although there is an overall shortage of scientific manpower, it may be that there are simply too many research scientists of a particular kind being produced in this country for the jobs available to them.

In each case I think it would be quite fair to claim that science teaching in one form or another should shoulder part of the responsibility for this state of affairs.

However, by far the most difficult problem for educators is to try to arrange for the right number of the right standard to find their way into the various professions which need early specialised training. This demands a very careful balance between the best interests of the individual and the requirements of the State. There cannot be a satisfactory solution if it is based on the personal attitude of a teacher toward a particular profession or what happens to be currently fashionable amongst sixth-formers.

I do not want to try and assess the relative weight of influence of teacher and parent in this, I am only referring to the teacher's share, whatever it may be.

Take, for example, the extraordinary situation in this country at the moment; people are crying out for University places, and yet there are a substantial number of vacancies in technological subjects, both at Universities and at Colleges of Advanced Technology – which amount to the same thing. Some put the vacancies as high as 3,000.

Places for pure science subjects on the other hand are just as over-subscribed as all the others. There may be many explanations for this, but I think it would be reasonable to suggest that if it is not some kind of misguided snobbery in parents it is probably due to the natural preference of teachers for pure science and their relative ignorance of technological subjects. I am quite sure that their influence is not deliberately against technology, but the effect is the same.

I cannot improve on a statement in the Science and Education Report of the Association for Science Education: 'To contribute to the development of his pupils in this broader way the new teacher will need to have done more than acquire a few rudimentary skills such as voice production, blackboard work and class management. He will need to have thought about his pupils as individuals, about personal relationships, about society, both local and general, about moral issues and the religious and philosophical grounds on which they have been judged. He must see how his teaching can contribute to the mental and moral wellbeing, as well as to the social and economic status of his pupils, of the Nation, and of mankind generally.'

All I would like to add is that I hope the people who sit on the numerous committees on scientific manpower and write those interesting reports will remember that their statistics are about people with individual souls and attitudes, no matter what level or kind of professional qualification they may have.

This business of attitude is very interesting. For instance, looking through some pamphlets on suggested science courses I was struck by the fact that they always refer to fundamental principles. It seems to me, for instance, that it would make more sense to students if you started by describing how a bicycle transmission worked, and then explained the principle on which it was based, rather than the other way round. I cannot help feeling that Boyle's law would be more intelligible if it was used to explain the operation of the internal combustion engine rather than as an unrelated scientific discovery. Most children have seen a car and used a bicycle but very few of them are capable of grasping an abstract principle.

I am only using this as an example to illustrate that the predilection for the fundamental is so strong in science teachers that the basic principle in all teaching – that is, proceeding from the known to the unknown – seems to have been overlooked. If this attitude towards fundamental laws in science is pursued right through the course it is not altogether surprising that students want to be pure scientists and continue with the same study, rather than take up technology, or applied science, which demands a particularly practical attitude towards problems.

The other remarkable situation is the shortage of science teachers. This at a time when so much of our material civilisation has been devised and is maintained and progressed by science and technology. What makes it even more difficult to understand is that the shortage exists in spite of considerable numbers taking pure science in the Universities who are, presumably, hoping for jobs in scientific research. Even when they cannot get those jobs they apparently prefer to emigrate rather than teach.

I do not think that the economic argument is the only one. I suspect that it is easier to be an average research worker than an average teacher. Whereas in the humanities it is possible to combine teaching at any level with the private pursuit of knowledge, in science this is virtually impossible owing to the need for complicated and expensive equipment. The result is that in science, of all the academic subjects, teaching and research tend to become divided.

Two things may help to improve matters. First there is the Nuffield grant of £250,000 for research into science teaching. The results of this, combined with the comments and experience of the Association for Science Education, should be very valuable. Secondly there are the Royal Society grants for scientific research in school laboratories, particularly aimed to allow teachers to go on doing original work.

Like science itself, the teaching of science must be continually on the move, adding the new-found facts and laws to its curriculum and also devising progressively better teaching methods. Even more important, it must be the means of feeding back into succeeding generations the attitudes to science which will ensure that our civilisation uses science in the right way. Without this feed-back the world may find itself spiralling to its own destruction.

From the Address to the
Members of the Association for
Science Education, London, April 26, 1963

THREE

The Impact of Science

THE HUMAN community experiences the impact of science in two ways.

In the first place there is the direct material impact which is obvious for all to see. Improved standards of medical treatment and public health; rapid communications and transport; a vast increase in agricultural and industrial productivity through machines and techniques developed from scientific ideas; a terrifying array of military weapons capable of widespread and, for the first time in history, permanent destruction; a very wide improvement and distribution in entertainment through radio, television, films and so on; and in general a whole mass of domestic equipment facilities and gadgets designed to make life easier and more comfortable.

Secondly, there is the indirect impact of science. This is less obvious but can be seen in two ways. There is the intellectual impact of scientific thought and discovery upon the minds of men previously dominated by superstition, tradition and old wives' tales due to the very natural absence of any knowledge of the true facts. The most typical example was the publication of Darwin's *Origin of Species* which introduced an element of fact and reason into a subject up till then reserved to religious tradition. This opened the minds and imaginations of a great many people to possibilities and ideas which had been denied to previous generations.

Although it is difficult to assess in precise terms, I believe that the influence of this scientific enlightenment upon the minds and thoughts of intelligent men and women is the most important impact that science has made upon the community as a whole.

In many respects this has had many excellent results but it has also encouraged a concentration upon the material things of this world at the expense of human and moral considerations. This, I think, is important because the future progress of mankind must be guided by human and moral ideals as well as by purely material ambitions.

The other way in which science has indirectly affected our lives is in the overall increase of the world's population and in the concentration of population around industrial areas. The former is due to better health and more food and the latter is due to increasing human dependence upon industrial employment.

Science has created this situation and now we are entirely dependent upon further scientific research to keep these vast cities and industries in a fit state to support healthy and prosperous human life.

The population of the world is increasing at such a fantastic rate that within a few years we shall be living an entirely different sort of existence. As the cities grow bigger, so the countryside will be pushed further and further away and people will be confined entirely within a man-made artificial environment. The demands of mankind for housing space, agriculture, transport systems and raw materials; the pollution of the atmosphere, the land, the water, even the sea; and perhaps the gradual alteration of the world's climatic conditions, will all have a profound effect upon what we now know as the natural world which has evolved over countless centuries.

Before scientific investigation came on the scene and before scientific ideas were applied on a large scale, all the processes of nature which occur on this earth were considered to be fixed, immutable and inevitable. Today, the factual knowledge of nature and our ability to control those natural processes have completely changed the situation. To begin with, the results of scientific research were used piecemeal as they became available. A little bit here in medicine; a little bit there in radio communications; small steps in agriculture; bigger steps in dyestuffs and synthetic materials. By degrees the results of research have begun to affect every aspect of human life.

Now we are slowly beginning to realise that we have in fact gained almost complete control of our environment. We are also beginning to realise that unless we are very careful indeed we can make serious and long-lasting mistakes in the indiscriminate application of scientific techniques.

The recognition of the tremendous power which science has put in our hands is creating a revolution in thought, just as great as that produced by Darwin. Already our outlook is changing. We do not accept any more, for example, that poverty, hunger, disease and ignorance are inevitable. We know we can do something about them. We have known about pollution for a long time; now we know we can put a stop to it. We know what is happening to the world but, what is even more important, we know that science has given us the opportunity and the power to control our own future.

The sort of power which mankind has gained through science demands an equally great sense of responsibility.

The problem we have to face is to decide fairly and honestly what sort of future we want without avoiding the difficult and awkward issues, and then to take active steps to plan for it. Instead of letting science have an indiscriminate and haphazard impact upon the world we must learn to use its power to create the sort of environment in which mankind, and all the living things which share this world with us, can thrive and prosper.

From the Address at the opening
of the London International Youth
Science Fortnight, July 22, 1963

FOUR

Communication

SCIENCE AND technology are barren unless they form a part of humanity's aspirations.

Every technology has some impact upon the human community but I would hazard that the technologists who serve the area of human communication have the most direct and the most important influence upon the development of human civilisation. Communication embraces several technologies, but radio engineering is rapidly becoming, if it is not already, the most important of them all. It has transformed all the previous methods of communication whether for entertainment, for business, for military purposes or between continents.

Marconi's faint message received at Signal Hill only sixty-four years ago opened the flood gates of radio engineering and today telecommunication techniques have achieved almost fantastic proportions.

Judging by the comments on the tyranny of the telephone and the tirades of the prophets of doom on the subject of television, there are obviously some who feel that, like Christopher Columbus, Marconi went rather too far!

Today micro-wave radio links using 2,000, 4,000 or 6,000 M/c's can transmit, for instance, either a single high-quality 625 line colour television signal or as many as 960 telephone conversations; or even, where required on certain main routes, 1,800 conversations. New forms of aerial are capable of being shared by many separate systems at common repeater points. The 600-foot tower for the London Post Office has been designed to house equipment and aerial systems covering London's long distance telephone circuit and television channel requirements for many years to come. It will eventually be able to handle up to 150,000 simultaneous telephone conversations as well as 40 or more channels for television. It is also not unreasonable to suppose that the present limit which is set by the radio frequency spectrum available for this purpose, could be doubled by new forms of modulation.

Added to this development in the means of communication by radio is the rapid development of techniques in data transmission. In a recent test with Telstar a rate of 870,000 bits per second were transmitted. At that rate the whole contents of the Bible could be transmitted in 45 seconds.

The transmission of television is assuming enormous proportions and in Britain about one third of all micro-wave and coaxial-cable wide-band channels are used for television. There are some 60 main line vision channels – totalling about 6,000 channel miles, carrying B.B.C. and I.T.A. programmes over the whole country. This has been rapidly extended with the introduction of B.B.C.2 on 625 lines and the prospect of more I.T.A. channels.

Further improvements are not far off. The transmission of very broad bands of frequencies of millimetre waves from 50,000 to 150,000 millions of cycles per second through wave guides.

A wave guide about two inches in diameter, with repeaters and other associated equipment every 20 miles, should be capable of providing a band width of 1,000 M/c's in each direction of transmission. This is equivalent to 250,000 speech circuits or 200 both-way television channels.

Then there is communication by means of coherent light beams generated by lasers and guided through reflective tubes. Colour television and inter-continental television through communication satellites is already with us and, together with information storage systems and learning machines, may easily transform our whole concept of education and of news-gathering and reporting.

The development of telecommunications through earth satellites produces some very interesting radio engineering problems. For instance, it is necessary to handle received signal levels on the earth's surface which are of the order of a tenth of a micro-micro watt. To do this requires the harnessing of widely divergent technologies ranging from precision structural engineering through real time digital computers and conventional telecommunication engineering to cryogenics.

The British Post Office Earth Station at Goonhilly, for instance, provided an opportunity for the exploration of masers which had previously been rather a scientific novelty. The essential parts of this type of amplifier operate in liquid helium a few degrees above absolute zero temperature.

Within the field of pure telecommunications the chief problem of satellite design yet to be solved is that of multiple access; that is to say the ability of several earth stations handling differing volumes of traffic to intercommunicate simultaneously through a satellite with which they have mutual visibility.

This brief survey of the present state of the art gives some idea of the tremendous developments in communication techniques which are taking place and which have to take place in order to keep up with the growing demand.

Yet all these developments are really only improvements upon previous methods. They take the place of verbal or written messages sent by runners with cleft sticks, or carrier pigeons or by ships. There are, however, two areas of communication where radio is not an improvement on a previous system but where it is the only system of communication, and therefore the whole undertaking is entirely dependent upon it.

First, the whole satellite and space-craft business depends upon radio links for communication and control; and, secondly, the operation of aircraft both military and civil would be quite impossible without radio communication, radio navigation and radio control circuits and landing aids. Every pilot has his own views about these things but my personal opinion is that the area coverage system of navigational aids will eventually become essential wherever there is a high density of air traffic. The point source system together with distance measuring equipment is easy and convenient but I doubt if it will be able to compete with the sort of densities at terminal points which are likely within a few years.

Radio has also made a profound impact on many other fields.

In the military sphere for instance rapid radio communication and detection by radar at sea, in the air and on land has transformed tactics; missile guidance and control is almost entirely by radio and as might be expected there is a whole new element for military activity in radio or more exactly, electronic warfare. Then again radio has provided an entirely new medium for scientific research and exploration into inter-galactic space.

I think I ought to add that radio has also added an entirely new dimension to international politics and national propaganda. You have only to spin the short wave dial to hear the 'party line' from a dozen countries in every language under the sun.

Australia has been making a very important contribution in the field of radio research in space. The 210-foot radio telescope belonging to the Radio Physics Laboratory of the C.S.I.R.O. and the Mills Cross radio telescope attached to Sydney University provide Australia with two immensely powerful research instruments. They are, of course, particularly important as they are situated in the southern hemisphere with its relatively unexplored field of activity.

These two telescopes and all the associated scientific effort have given Australia and especially Australian radio-physicists and engineers a very high reputation in the world.

The performance of the 210-foot telescope has exceeded the design specifications in all respects and in two years of operation the telescope has yielded important and often dramatic results. Many of these can be attributed to some unique feature of the instrument such as the high gain or resolving power, the wide range of wavelengths over which it is possible to make useful observations, or the precision of its motion.

In every respect this instrument reflects the highest credit on all the designers and engineers who have been responsible for its many remarkable features.

It is a fairly sobering thought that all these forms of communication, detection, and exploration, which form such an enormous slice of what has become accepted as everyday life, are so utterly dependent upon the technology of radio engineering. Several things flow from this. In the first place the standard of reliability of equipment must achieve a very high order because failure is no longer inconvenient, failure means disaster. For instance, any system of wholly automatic blind landing equipment for big passenger aircraft must obviously have a reliability which is several orders of magnitude greater than would be necessary in any previous equipment. It only needs the communications to fail in a space-craft and the whole mission becomes a failure.

Secondly, reliability cannot be achieved by making components bigger and stronger because the weight and space penalty in all these applications is critical. This in turn has been responsible for the evolution of transistors, semi-conductors, printed, evaporated and solid circuits and all the other results of micro-miniaturisation. These techniques have been developed to save weight and space and to increase reliability where this is vital but no one quite knows yet what the fall-out of this new technology is going to be. Smaller radios and television sets are obvious but there is really a limit to that sort of thing unless we start training mice to operate the micro-miniature controls.

The whole field of medical electronics already owes much to these techniques. Built-in pacemakers for the heart and regulators of various kinds, the control of artificial limbs and perhaps small built-in oxygen extractors for use under water instead of the cumbersome aqualung equipment. Certainly every kind of electronic control and computing equipment will benefit from these techniques, and one can only hope that some developments will be of direct use to the public at large.

Sir Edward Appleton in his Graham Clark Lecture put it this way:

'The feature of these recent developments I want to stress is the way that science and engineering have worked in partnership. Not only have we witnessed enormous mechanical engineering developments in the launching of huge vehicles into space and their subsequent orientation and control in desired orbits; there have also been revolutionary developments in electronic circuit design with miniaturized components.'

The point is that we are rapidly approaching the time when almost anything is possible. Existing knowledge and techniques are such that the only limit to scientific progress and material development is the human capacity to think up new ideas.

This is a wonderful situation for the scientist because it means that technology can provide him with the means to carry out virtually any piece of investigation. However, the technologist faces a rather more difficult problem when it comes to producing the means for the material progress of mankind. The most profitable are not necessarily the most socially valuable developments. But whatever the reason: profitability, social need, or defence, there are two sides to any successful development.

The first difficulty is to see the problem, to become aware of a need, to visualise the possibility of some improvement in the present way of doing things. This requires people with some very particular characteristics. It needs imagination, for instance, and an understanding of people and the whole pattern of existence of the human community. Furthermore, it needs a broad understanding of technology as a whole and industrial processes in particular. All these things are necessary because if the benefits of scientific knowledge and technological advance are to be used to the best advantage they must be applied in those areas where they can do most good. Otherwise a lot of relatively useless and fearfully complicated and expensive gadgets are going to be produced merely because it is technically possible to do so. You do not have to look far for evidence of this sort of spurious progress.

The other side of this situation is the problem of design. Once the demand for a particular piece of equipment has been stated someone has to sit down and design it. I do not know if there is in fact one perfect design solution to any given problem but the important thing is that just any design, provided it works, is not necessarily the best design. Motor-cars are a good example. The principles of all the component parts are well known and yet some cars are better than others. The difference lies in the choice of the design solution by the designer.

The more technical and complicated our civilisation becomes the more important is the function of the designer. No longer does he have to make do with the limited range of natural materials, neither is he bounded by empirical laws of construction. Today the designer has a vast mass of information, materials and techniques at his command and a frightening array of test equipment to show him where he has gone wrong. None of this can solve his problem for him, for that he must rely upon his intellect and on his human judgement and experience.

It follows from this that purely technical education and training are not enough preparation for technological designers. They need a special outlook and characteristics which must be given the opportunity to develop concurrently with their technical training.

This applies to radio engineering as much, if not more than, to any other technology because of its direct impact upon the human community. These two factors – stating the problem and designing the solution – are relevant throughout the whole range of radio technology from scientific instruments through to domestic equipment.

Naturally I am not suggesting that radio engineers should be responsible for the information or the entertainment which passes through their equipment. What I am suggesting is that designers of radio equipment, knowing the potential of their technology, should seek out those areas of development which are most helpful to mankind. For example the development of cheap and reliable radio-telephone equipment has transformed life in the outback of Australia and many other similar areas. This kind of development may not be very profitable but in terms of human progress it has an incalculable value. Technologists must always be aware of the needs of people and particularly the needs of minorities. Profitability may be the most compelling reason for development but I see no reason why science and technology should not have a social conscience as well.

Just one more point about the importance of recognising the problem and designing the solution. Many people living in this world are fully conversant with modern gadgets and quite accustomed to their use even if they have not the least idea how they work. However, there are even more people who are still completely cut off for all practical purposes from every manifestation of modern technology. In the technically advanced countries the human communities developed together with science and technology from the very beginning and are therefore far more capable of accepting further changes and improvements. Those communities which are still relatively unaffected by modern technology would be liable to severe disruption if they were suddenly exposed to the full force of modern material existence. The difficulty here is the selection of progressively more complicated technical equipment which can be introduced into their system of life and which will be most useful without causing unreasonable social stresses.

We have always tended to assume that any discovery or invention, so long as it was conveniently labour-saving, was naturally a boon to the world and to humanity. We measure progress by the speed of aircraft or by the number of television channels on the dial. We are obsessed by our material welfare to the exclusion of all concern for the social development of mankind. We may have discovered the existence of radio sources several million light years away with an immensely clever piece of equipment but we continue to treat each other and all the other living things on our planet in a way which is only a bare improvement on primitive man. At least in the primitive state mankind could only do a limited amount of damage. The same will and emotions which caused primitive man to damage and destroy are still with us today with the only difference that technology has given us vastly improved means to give expression to our anger and jealousy, our pride and covetousness. We can control everything in our world except ourselves.

I sympathise with the view that we must go on discovering new facts about the universe and I appreciate the excitement of probing even further into the frontiers of knowledge. It is true that without this persistent investigation we would not know half the disturbing facts about our occupation of the earth, but it seems to me that unless we make a very determined effort to sort out the problems created by man in his occupation of this earth it is very unlikely that further scientific exploration will be either necessary or possible.

I want to suggest that scientific and technological progress is not only valueless, it is actively harmful, unless it is modified or directed by a social and humanitarian outlook. Scientists and engineers must also give their attention to the really serious problems facing humanity even if it means giving up some problems which seem to be more interesting or profitable. Equally the intellectual humanist can no longer pretend that science and technology are incapable of making a valuable contribution to the progress of human civilisation.

Although the scientific and technological revolution is by far the greatest influence upon the progress of modern human civilisation, scientists and technologists cannot shoulder the whole responsibility for the direction mankind takes in the future. Every individual has some responsibility but in particular much depends upon enlightened civil servants; upon industrial and commercial administrators with a strong sense of humanity and an understanding of the possibilities and limitations of technology. Above all it depends on the decision-makers, the national Governments and the international agencies. Only the combination of all these groups can ensure that the world advances to a higher standard of civilisation.

If we are ever going to attempt to solve the problems of over-population, under-employment and malnutrition; if we are ever to make industry the slave and not the master of the human community, if we are to develop a social system which is rid of unnatural pressures and the corrupting influence of boredom and frustration; if we are to save what is left of the remainder of the living creatures on the earth, the whole weight of scientific, technological and intellectual humanism must join together in a single campaign.

The present state of development of radio engineering demonstrates the fantastic achievements of which the human brain and organisation are capable. This same standard of talent must be applied to the development and control of our human environment, otherwise all the discoveries of science will be sterile and all the skills of the technologist will be wasted.

From the Inaugural Dunrossil Memorial Lecture
at the Institute of Radio and Electronics Engineers,
Australia, February 23, 1965

FIVE

Human and Material Resources

I AM GOING to take it for granted that it is generally accepted that development in the broadest sense is a good thing. I hope I can assume that mankind is better off with proper food, sanitation, housing and all the material comforts which modern science, engineering and industry can provide. I am not assuming, however, that this material development necessarily implies a higher standard of human civilisation. This, I believe, depends upon qualities of the mind and spirit which are not directly related to material comfort and convenience.

Given the need for development in the material sense it does not take a great stretch of the imagination to visualise the engineer's part in the process. There are, in particular, four ways in which the engineer can implement and influence development:

1. By continually finding practical ways and means of applying scientific principles and discoveries in power, industry, transportation, communication and construction. This means that research establishments are needed in all the divisions of engineering so that practising engineers can apply the benefits of fundamental scientific research.

2. By the application of the latest and most efficient methods to individual projects. This means that practising engineers must have some way of keeping up to date.

3. By the careful administration, maintenance and improvement of the engineering complex. Building or developing some project from scratch may have a great many difficulties but maintaining and improving a project which has been in existence for many years calls for even more skill and administrative ability. Railways are an obvious example.

4. By the technical training and education of the next generation of engineers. This is very much the engineer's responsibility and whatever the rewards of practice may be nothing is more worthwhile in the long run than teaching the next generation.

The engineer is in fact the means by which the people are able to enjoy the fruits of science, whether in building new projects, or in maintaining and keeping up to date what is already in existence. I need hardly list the highly developed communities of history which decayed for the lack of engineers to keep their great works in operation.

Simple technical know-how is also not enough. In order to make a really worthwhile contribution the engineer needs the vision to appreciate what is possible as well as the technique to realise his dream.

It is also wrong to assume that the engineer is simply concerned with material gadgetry or the purely practical and commercial side of life. All large-scale projects and modernisation plans are bound to have a profound and lasting influence upon the lives of very great numbers of people. Unless their conception, execution and running are all based upon a practical humanity they will contribute very little to man's progress.

That is why technological training must be combined with a broad general education. Each generation must learn that technical knowledge without a sense of mission and responsibility is wasted. Education which merely produces a sense of dissatisfaction and frustration and a kind of topsy-turvy snobbery about what is suitable and unsuitable employment is a failure. The system must instil a sense of the value of engineering to human development so that people come to look upon it with the same sense of service as missionaries and doctors.

At the root of all development are the nations' natural resources, they are the raw materials with which engineers have to work in order to fill the basic needs of the peoples of the world. Food depends on agriculture and increased agricultural productivity depends on agricultural machinery, irrigation, food processing and transport. Industry depends upon power and upon the extraction and transport of its raw materials. Industrial processing itself depends upon the engineer as do the invention and design of those gadgets which are intended to help or entertain the public at large. On top of that lies the very important responsibility of teaching the next generation of engineers in such a way that they can progress from past techniques and build on past experience.

The wealth of a nation, and all which that implies, depends upon the efficient organisation of its resources both natural and industrial as well as human.

The engineer in turn has two kinds of resources with which to work. There are the renewable resources; by which I mean those which grow or which are renewed by the climate, and non-renewable resources, those which are extracted once and for all.

Luckily in supplying humanity's basic need of adequate food the resources are not only renewable but the area which can grow them, as well as the quantity from a given area, can be substantially increased by modern engineering and scientific methods. This is particularly fortunate because no country can hope to reap the benefits of industrialisation without a sufficient and cheap supply of food for both the rural and urban population. Secondly if the world's food resources had a known limit at this time the tremendous increase in the population of the world would pose an insoluble problem. As it is things are difficult enough. Dr Norman Wright of the F.A.O. has estimated that the world population will have grown from 3,000 million in 1961 to 4,000 million in 1980 and 6,000 million in 2000. On the basis of bringing the average world diet to a reasonable level by 1980 he has suggested that we must increase the world's cereal production by 33 per cent and the world's production of milk, meat, eggs and fish by not less than 100 per cent. By the year 2000, the figures are a 100 per cent increase for cereals and 200 per cent for animal products.

Dr Wright has based these figures on a broad estimate that the food supplies of countries representing 60 per cent of the world's population fall below 2,200 calories per day of which nearly half are below 2,000 – a figure which is 800 calories less than that at which British adults and children start to lose weight.

This situation is even worse than it sounds because in most under-developed countries there are inadequacies in quality as well as quantity of food, with the result that the people suffer from malnutrition as well as under-nutrition. In North America for instance only 25 per cent of the diet is in starchy foods while in Africa it is 66 per cent and in the Far East it rises to 73 per cent.

I want to introduce a few more revealing statistics. The Commonwealth fraction of the world land area is 23 per cent and the fraction of the world population is 24 per cent. Even though Britain has the highest population density, 68 per cent of the Commonwealth population is in India and Pakistan. Out of a total Commonwealth population of 682 million no less than 56 per cent are employed in agriculture – 5 per cent of Britain's, 12 per cent of Australia's and 71 per cent of India's. The really interesting part of that comparison is that agriculture, forestry and fishing employ

5 per cent and are worth 4 per cent of the gross domestic product in Britain. Australia employs 12 per cent which produces 17 per cent, whereas in India 71 per cent of the population only produce 47 per cent of the gross domestic product. This shows very clearly that great strides are possible in agricultural productivity.

As I have said, for the time being we are also fortunate that the land area for agriculture can be increased. In fact 44 per cent of the Commonwealth land area is either unused, built-on or wasteland. This figure needs to be qualified, however, because one fifth of the undeveloped land surface is too cold, one fifth too arid, one fifth is mountains and one tenth has no soil. This leaves about 30 per cent as potentially cultivatable and gives some idea of the scope for bringing deserts, equatorial forest and tropical grasslands into production, and the tremendous contribution which engineering can make to agriculture.

Four things are needed to stimulate and increase agricultural productivity:

1. Extend the area under cultivation which generally means the provision of water in dry areas, the removal of water in swampy areas, and the control of pests, diseases and weeds.

2. Increase the productivity of the soil by applying more nutrients. This is the first impact of industry proper upon agriculture because plants need fixed nitrogen, phosphorus and potassium which have to go through some sort of industrial process before they are usable.

3. Better equipment for use on the land so that together with the increased use of fertilisers the output per acre can be substantially improved. In the industrially developed countries very sophisticated machinery is needed to increase the output per man. In the less developed countries the emphasis should be on improved design of simple instruments. Remember the groundnut scheme which prompted the remark 'Give us the job and we will finish the tools.'

4. A system of agricultural organisation which will make it worthwhile for the rural population to grow food for sale. This includes the organisation of land tenure, proper transport and marketing facilities and a comprehensive advisory service.

It is no use attempting any or all of these things without taking human nature into account. These points may be self-evident to an outsider but you cannot, without much suffering, force human nature to accept a complete change – even for the better – of the basis of its existence overnight. The art in this case is to reconcile the interests of the individual with the interests of the state.

Much progress has already been made and if we learn from the successes even more rapid progress is possible in the future.

It is only necessary to look at the tremendously high agricultural productivity of New Zealand to realise what can be done under very favourable conditions. The Gezira cotton scheme in the Sudan is an excellent example of all the points I mentioned, while the huge irrigation schemes in India and Pakistan are both an encouragement and a warning. Warning because the early schemes have given rise to water-logging and salinity which are taking as many acres out of production as new schemes are bringing in. New methods of irrigation, drainage and tube wells are now beginning to overcome these problems. I visited the Land Reclamation Laboratories in Lahore and gained some idea of the complexity and magnitude of their task. In addition to recovery of previously productive land there are plans to bring a further 9½ million acres in Pakistan into production by irrigation. Even so the race between the growth of population and the provision of additional resources is desperately close.

Even without mechanisation or increasing the area under cultivation productivity can be very greatly improved by the application of fertiliser and trace elements where necessary. This operation, however, depends upon the cheap and therefore industrial production of fertiliser which in turn depends upon cheap power. For this purpose the natural gas fields of Pakistan are most convenient as they supply both the power and the raw material for fertiliser production.

Taking all this into account it is rather sobering to find that the Commonwealth share of the world's food production is not very impressive. Of the basic foods only rice, 24 per cent, barley, 20 per cent, and mutton, 23 per cent, are in proportion to our population. All the others are way below 20 per cent of the world's output. Coarse grains are only 9 per cent, pigmeat is 5 per cent and wheat 14 per cent. This is in spite of the fact that many areas in Commonwealth countries regularly produce two and sometimes three crops per year already.

From what I have said I need hardly emphasise what is expected of engineers for agriculture especially in the less developed countries.

The next stage after food production is food preservation. There are one or two old-established methods of preserving food but generally speaking the whole technique of food preservation is due to modern engineering methods. It has even gained the title of food technology and not even the homely and old-fashioned smoking and curing methods have managed to escape the food engineers.

Food technology is already most important in keeping out undesirable organisms. It is going to become even more important in tropical countries which are rapidly developing huge concentrations of population. This whole field of the preservation and distribution of food is wide open to the engineer. Freezing, canning, curing, spray and freeze drying, ionising radiation and every kind of processing are all engineering problems.

Lastly, I think it is generally recognised that our harvest of food from the sea is still very under-developed. Both the methods of extraction and control could be considerably improved by modern equipment and scientific study.

Hand in hand with agriculture to supply the world's basic needs is energy. Energy is the very basis of modern civilisation. Whichever way you look at it cheap, convenient and abundant power ranks with food as a means to raise standards of living.

The non-renewable sources of energy are coal, oil and natural gas. The renewable sources are the sun, wind, water, wood, cow-dung and ultimately the breeder reactor in nuclear power. Also for the time being a very large proportion of the energy requirements for transport and agriculture is met by animal power in the shape of horses, oxen, camels, donkeys and elephants.

Distributed power in the form of electricity and gas, and independent power units in the form of internal combustion engines, are essential to high productivity in agriculture, transport and industry, and most convenient for personal use in the home and on the roads.

The point about all this is that there is a close relationship between the amount of energy available per head of the population and the state of material development of a country.

The explanation is obvious. Power for irrigation pumps and fertiliser factories raises agricultural productivity. Power for transport distributes agricultural products, brings raw materials to industry, distributes industrial products and transforms individual mobility. Power for industry makes it possible to harvest or extract the raw materials with greater efficiency and it is the very life blood of industrial processing and manufacture.

Here I must again plunge into some figures in order to give an outline of the energy situation in the Commonwealth. As I have already said, the Commonwealth proportion of the world population is 24 per cent and the Commonwealth covers 23 per cent of the world's land area. Add to this the fact that 20 per cent of the world's land rainfall falls on, and 18 per cent of the seventeen great rivers of the world flow through, Commonwealth countries. Finally, and most significantly, the production of energy by the Commonwealth is only 12 per cent of the world's production even though India and probably several others have doubled their output in the last five years.

This figure of 12 per cent has to be reduced to 10 per cent if you leave out the oil produced in Bahrein, Kuwait and Qatar and it means that Commonwealth countries at present only produce 3.5 per cent of the world's oil and 3 per cent of the natural gas.

Looked at in this way it is obvious that there is a very real urgency to increase the energy production and distribution in the Commonwealth.

In this field the engineer has almost unlimited scope and the solution of this energy problem demands more than skill and intelligence, it demands the services of far-sighted engineering administrators to exploit every indigenous source of energy and to plan the most economic form of energy production from other sources.

Australia for instance is very short of water for all purposes. The Snowy River Scheme will do much to meet immediate demands for energy and irrigation but there are virtually no other sources of hydro-electric energy on the continent. Fortunately she has considerable resources for the production of nuclear energy.

New Zealand on the other hand has fairly large reserves of water power but they happen to be on the South Island whereas the majority of the population is on the North Island. I see that the New Zealand Government are about to call for tenders to lay power cables across the Cook Strait.

Engineers have also made it possible to harness to energy production the geothermal steam in the North Island which was otherwise merely a pleasant tourist attraction.

India has great reserves of coal but they happen to be mostly on one side of the sub-continent while power is badly needed in many distant places which have no alternative sources. Unfortunately the cost of transporting the coal or the electrical energy is prohibitive so that there may be openings here for nuclear power stations.

In Canada the situation is that 85 per cent of her electricity is provided by hydro-electric stations and she has still only tapped 28 per cent of her resources of water power. I flew over the Hamilton Falls in Northern Quebec not long ago and I am not surprised that the engineers have cast covetous eyes on so much energy going to waste.

Power is related to industrial productivity but cheap power can also attract industry. In Ghana I saw the site for the Volta River Dam which will make it possible to exploit the bauxite deposits not far away for conversion into aluminium. The giant Kariba Dam on the Zambesi will give a tremendous stimulus to primary and secondary industry.

I have only referred to the large members of the Commonwealth. It is worth remembering that the smaller places have even more urgent problems without the material or economic resources with which to solve them. The Atlantic and Pacific islands need energy badly but, unless they can harness the wind, the sun, or the tides, there is little scope for development.

Resources can only be converted into useable products by manufacturing industry. Unfortunately it is becoming increasingly popular to look upon industry merely as a convenient way of giving employment. Industry does undoubtedly give employment but that is not its basic function. Industry exists for three reasons:

1. It produces those things which are needed by a community to live a reasonably comfortable existence.

2. It also produces those things which though not essential to human existence are very nice to have.

3. It produces things which can be sold to other countries, preferably at an overall profit.

I think it goes without saying that industry must also produce all those things which are needed by industry at all stages of the industrial process. In the less developed countries the first stage is the extraction of raw materials for use or export, followed by the production of the basic requirements of the manufacturing industries.

Industry has to satisfy the needs of the state as well as the needs and desires of the individual. In fact it is only by maintaining a proper balance between production for home consumption and production for export that a nation can maintain the upward curve of its standards of living. An adverse balance throws it upon the charity of more efficient or fortunate nations while a too favourable balance will merely widen the gap in standards between itself and its less efficient or fortunate neighbours. There can be no doubt that in the long run there is a greater chance of avoiding conflict if the material standards of people throughout the world are reasonably comparable.

It is difficult and probably misleading to try to generalise about the overall position of industry in the Commonwealth. In spite of that proviso, it is worth mentioning that in the renewable raw materials – other than food – production varies from 84 per cent of the world's jute to 51 per cent of wool to 11 per cent of cotton and 10 per cent of timber. In mining the Commonwealth produces only 12 per cent of the world's iron ore but more than its share of many other metallic ores. I have no figures for the manufacturing industries as a whole but it is significant that the Commonwealth produces only 11 per cent of the world's steel, 15 per cent of the aluminium and 11 per cent of man-made fibres.

If you take this in conjunction with the fact that in only five major Commonwealth countries do the manufacturing industries account for more than 20 per cent of the gross domestic product while in at least six countries agriculture and forestry account for more than 40 per cent of the gross domestic product, as well as the fact that we only produce 12 per cent of the world's energy, the picture comes into rather sharper focus.

The implication is that in agriculture, basic industries and energy the Commonwealth output is not in proportion to its area or population.

I have already dealt with the energy picture and with certain exceptions there seems to be no reason why the Commonwealth as a whole should not produce its proper share of energy, but nuclear power will be necessary to achieve this in many areas.

Much the same applies to agriculture but there the picture is rather distorted by the Indian sub-continent and Africa where at the moment there is a very high proportion of subsistence farming.

In mining the possibilities are very difficult to assess but it would seem that we have hardly begun to tap the known mineral resources of Canada and Australia.

The total resources of the Commonwealth are probably roughly in proportion to its size but this does not mean that the resources are evenly distributed. Each country has certain limiting factors and may lack certain raw materials but on the other hand most countries have probably got something which is needed or wanted by others. There is no absolute need for countries to be self-sufficient, the real need is for Commonwealth countries to co-operate in such a way that the people can enjoy a reasonable standard of existence and the chance to develop their talents and their resources for the common good.

This means that methods of extraction, methods of refining, methods of processing and the transport system are the factors which can turn deposits of natural resources into wealth producing assets. Where these are lacking – and this is by and large the situation in Britain – the only solution is the highest development of the human resources by a very advanced system of education and training. All these are problems for the engineer and the success with which they are tackled by imaginative engineers can transform the whole picture of industrial and economic activity in Commonwealth countries.

Having outlined the contribution which engineers can make to the development of agriculture, energy and industry in the Commonwealth, I must quickly add that none of their efforts would bear any fruit without an adequate system of transport and communications. It is virtually impossible to develop natural resources, or improve and augment the food situation, or even to enjoy the benefits of industrial enterprise without a comprehensive network of public and commercial transport and communications.

Indeed transport and communications are the means whereby the whole process of development is given purpose and direction and the only way by which the people can begin to adapt themselves to changing circumstances.

A community which is without the proper means of movement and contact is cut off from the world and therefore can only exist upon its own – usually very limited – resources. It cannot co-operate with its neighbours and its intellectual level is also bound to be restricted. As communications develop so its limit of experience is increased until it reaches the point where it is connected by the fastest transport and a virtually instantaneous communication system to all the other developed and mutually interdependent communities in the world.

Roads and paths made it possible for villages to co-operate, railways made it possible for districts to work together, while ships and aircraft have brought whole continents into contact for trade and commerce.

In the same way telegraphs and telephones, radio and newspapers are removing the barriers of ignorance and bringing the nations into closer concern with each other's problems.

Trade brought the old Empire into existence and communications kept it together. Now that it has become a Commonwealth of nations, transport and communications are making it possible to co-operate in every field of endeavour to the mutual advantage of all members.

A measure of the importance we attach to transport and communications in Britain is the amount of time and space devoted to its discussion. Anyone can start an argument any time by just mentioning British Railways or British roads. And yet it is only 602 miles from Land's End direct to John O'Groats and that's as far as you can go in these islands overland. If the Shetlands are included it makes a total of 768 miles. Compare this with Halifax to Vancouver, 2,850 miles, or Perth to Sydney, 2,030 miles. To cover areas of this size with a network of roads and railways is a staggering task and yet it must be done if development is to take place.

I sometimes wonder whether our transport engineers are fully aware of this enormous difference in scale between the problems of transport and communications in these islands compared to the larger Commonwealth countries.

There are similar difficulties in air transport. The distances, geography and climate in Britain are so different from other Commonwealth countries that it is not altogether surprising that there is an entirely different attitude to flying.

In Australia, India, Africa and Canada flying conditions, though uncomfortable at times and impossible for short periods, are such that aircraft can be operated for all purposes almost all the year round. As it is, the internal – or outback – flying in those countries is not unlike a country bus service. It certainly could not be more different from the sophisticated international air passenger systems which use the London airports.

This difference between British conditions and conditions in other Commonwealth countries also applies to aviation for agricultural purposes. Although there is a certain amount of agricultural aviation in Britain it is nothing at all compared to the potential employment of aircraft for this purpose in most Commonwealth countries.

The British aircraft industry is the most highly developed in the Commonwealth for the time being but it cannot hope to continue to play a major part in the development of the Commonwealth unless it has the services of imaginative engineers who understand the needs and the conditions of the other Commonwealth countries.

We have certainly not reached the end in the development of transport systems. Aircraft capable of vertical take-off and landing, blind landing systems, monorails, flat electro-magnetic traction and air-cushion craft are all waiting to be converted into economic possibilities by engineers.

The Hovercraft type of vehicle in particular may easily revolutionise overland transport in the more remote regions of many Commonwealth countries. Its major advantage as I see it is that there is no need for expensive ground installations such as roads or railway lines. So long as the track is reasonably level and the gradients not too severe these craft ought to be able to operate over almost all kinds of country. In Canada, for instance, summer transport in the north is by barge up rivers and lakes. During the winter it is by caterpillar drawn sled-trains. The Hovercraft ought to be able to operate equally easily summer and winter over snow and ice or water and land.

If this sort of craft has a reasonable operating economy there would seem to be openings for it in the outback of Australia, in Africa and in parts of India and Pakistan. In Bengal roads and railways have to be raised to keep them clear of flooding, and if they are to cross the Ganges delta or serve the islands in it, the bridge building programme alone would be extremely expensive. Under these circumstances an amphibious vehicle riding on an air-cushion might have considerable advantages.

In sea transport conditions are of course much the same all over the world. From the engineer's point of view therefore the two most fruitful fields of activity are in the process of shipbuilding and in the facilities for cargo-handling both in ships and ashore.

Distance, geography and weather do not make quite such a difference to communications although here again the pattern of press, radio and television development in Britain is governed by distance. Commonwealth countries have their own particular problems but the need for posts and telegraphs, telephones, radio, press and television is just as great in those countries and their development and installation is another of the engineer's tasks and responsibilities.

All progress in engineering ultimately depends upon Scientific Research. There are two aspects as far as the engineer is concerned. First, there is the fundamental and applied research which provides the engineer with new materials and techniques and with new applications of known principles. Secondly, there are the huge research instruments which have to be designed and built by engineers to enable the scientist to continue his investigations.

Many of the great strides in engineering history were made before scientific research was used deliberately to find new techniques. In recent times, however, we have come to think of science as producing the new ideas and engineering as the means of exploiting them. So much so that we are inclined to forget that much scientific research is only possible with the aid of very advanced engineering. Computers, electron microscopes, accelerators, radio telescopes and satellites are no longer bits of apparatus that can be knocked up in the lab. All these instruments and many others are the products of a highly sophisticated engineering industry.

As the developing countries begin to establish their own basic and applied research organisations and their own centres of advanced teaching, these complicated instruments will be in great demand and it is reasonable to suppose that they will get more rather than less complicated in the future.

Applied scientific and industrial research is essential in every country, if only because the conditions and the industrial activities vary in each country and it can well be argued that the developing countries should not spend their time on basic research until they have established a comprehensive applied and industrial research organisation.

From a practical point of view this is probably quite right but on the other hand it would be a mistake to deny those people who are both capable and determined to do basic research the means to do their work in their own country. One or two nationally and internationally known figures in advanced science or engineering can do a very great deal by their example to enhance the reputation of science and engineering in the eyes of their fellow countrymen and abroad.

Whatever science may do it is still essential to arrange for the education and training of the next generation but one of the problems of engineering education is that it covers such a wide field. It includes everything from science to manual skill. It can be sub-divided into a number of specialisations and yet none of them is any use by itself and all must have a proper appreciation of the part which engineering as a whole plays in the organisation of modern life and in future development.

This problem of higher education and technical training cannot be solved once and for all. Every country in the Commonwealth should look forward to progressive development which means that plans for education must look ahead to the needs of the next generation.

It is quite useless for the more fortunate countries to offer their help in building dams, power stations and factories if the managers and engineers needed to operate them are not available. Furthermore, it does not take very long to put up the physical structures but it may take anything up to fifteen years for the people to gain sufficient knowledge and experience to run them.

If the various aid programmes are to be of any lasting value, there must be a strong emphasis on technical education. Colleges, equipment and teachers are all badly needed and teachers in particular will be needed for a great many years to come. This means that those countries with well-established higher technical educational facilities must take this added responsibility into consideration. Providing places for other Commonwealth citizens is only a temporary emergency solution; in the long run engineers and technicians must have their basic training in their own countries.

The significance of all this is that development and progress cannot be maintained unless there are enough people in the next generation capable of carrying on the work. Only engineers themselves are capable of estimating what a nation's future needs are likely to be in graduates and technicians. Only engineers can decide what the qualifications should be in the light of the current state of engineering development. Only engineers who have themselves been properly educated can begin to impart the necessary knowledge into the next generation. It is not simply a matter of maintaining standards of knowledge and conduct, it means that they are ultimately responsible for the material well-being of their fellow citizens.

In order to do this some sort of professional organisation is necessary.

In our system – and it also applies to several other Commonwealth countries – most professions are self-governing with very considerable powers over their members. Entrance is controlled by examination, professional ethics and practice are carefully watched and the whole tone of the profession is set by the professional organisation.

In a profession such as engineering, which covers such an immense field of activities, there are bound to be an increasing number of specialisations. Even so I believe that all the specialists would agree that there is a general background common to them all. The thing to remember is that in education we all start off equally ignorant and only gradually build up a specialist knowledge. Then, as administrative duties increase and specialist knowledge tends to get a bit out of date, the importance of individual specialisation gradually gets less and appreciation of other specialisations tends to grow.

Any large engineering project must depend for its planning and successful completion on the closest possible co-operation and integration of many specialists. When it comes to exporting engineering the tendency is for Governments to commission a complete project – or package deal – from another Government or from a group or consortium of companies.

By the nature of things each Commonwealth country is bound to develop certain engineering specialities. For instance Canada has already gained considerable experience in hydro-electric work, India is deeply involved in irrigation problems, New Zealand is very advanced in dairy technology. If the Commonwealth is to make the most of these varied talents it is essential that the professional institutions should make determined and continuous efforts to keep in close contact with each other.

Different people may expect different things from engineers. I have suggested that they are necessary to meet humanity's basic needs of food and power, to develop and at the same time to conserve natural resources, to exploit the advantages of the industrial process and to enable science to continue its investigations. Their original thought and technical management are the main factors in a nation's prosperity. In fact while doctors are responsible for the bodily welfare of people, the engineer is responsible for the material welfare of nations. This is a very wide responsibility but unless it is recognised by all the organisations which have the duty of educating engineers they will fail to turn out people capable of giving direction and purpose to the progress of the world.

From the Seventh Graham Clark Lecture,
'The Engineer in Commonwealth Development',
the Institutions of Civil, Mechanical and Electrical
Engineers, London, April 13, 1961

SIX

The Nuclear Dilemma

THERE CAN be no doubt that technologies change social and cultural patterns, but then, for example, so do crimes or wealth. However, it is worth bearing in mind that technologies are not developed with the express purpose of changing society or culture. The primary object is to meet perceived practical human needs. Vastly improved standards of transport and communications, public health and hygiene, housing and household gadgets, inevitably change ways of life. All these can raise material standards of living, and they certainly make it possible to increase the quantity of human inhabitants of this earth, but there is no evidence to suggest that they improve the quality of human behaviour or stimulate greater artistic talents.

Quite apart from the social and cultural consequences of modern technology, there is another area that is very significantly affected by technologies and which in turn influences the living population of the world. Modern technologies have created a growing demand for the earth's resources, and they have also developed the means to acquire those resources at an ever-increasing rate. And in the long run – that is if there is to be a long run – common sense suggests that demand will have to be balanced against the sustainable availability of renewable resources. In that sense the success of modern technology poses a very important challenge to human ingenuity and an even greater challenge to the present generation for the future of all life on earth.

I do not think that any discussion about modern technology can ignore what is certainly the most important challenge of modern technology to mankind: namely the development of the generation of power from nuclear reactors and of nuclear weapons. Both these products of technology pose baffling dilemmas. Evidence suggests that conventional power stations, together with some of the industries they supply, plus vehicle emissions, are mainly responsible for the acid rain which is destroying forests and killing life in rivers and lakes throughout the Northern latitudes. Nuclear power stations may pose other problems, but they do not produce acid rain. Then again, all the evidence points to the successful deterrent effect of nuclear weapons. Although they do not stop small wars or the invasion by stronger powers of their weaker neighbours, they have prevented escalation, and they certainly appear to have discouraged armed conflict between East and West in Europe. Yet many people still seem fervently to believe that wars are created by weapons. The trouble is that any weapon capable of killing is dangerous the moment it gets into the hands of anyone with the intention of using it. For nearly a hundred years Britain had a naval fleet more powerful than those of the rest of the world put together, but it was not called up to go to war until 1914. What is known to the Jewish people as the Holocaust was perpetrated without the use of any military weapons at all. More people have been killed by motor-cars or by terrorism than by bombs dropped in war.

Most people know that the destructive power of nuclear weapons is vastly, almost immeasurably, greater than that of conventional weapons. Therefore in all logic there is really no point in having any more of these weapons than the bare minimum to provide a credible deterrent. But what really matters are the scruples of their possessors, the character of those individuals with the ultimate power to unleash them. People are far more dangerous than inanimate objects.

Many years ago Albert Einstein said that nuclear power had changed everything, and added significantly 'except our way of thinking'. It is tempting to suggest that nuclear weapons are the ultimate social and cultural challenge of modern technology, but it would not be quite accurate. The challenge is not to such abstract concepts as society or culture. The challenge is directly to our human nature and to the way we think and the way we use our brains. The question is whether the threat of cataclysmic disaster can possibly bring those traditional origins of conflict, human greed, ambition and good intentions, under some sort of rational restraint and control.

From the Address to the Fellowship of Engineering,
London, April 26, 1983

SEVEN

Conservation

IT IS becoming painfully obvious that unless the major land-users – that is, agriculturalists of all kinds, farmers, land reclamation, irrigation commissions, foresters, mineral developers, water and power engineers, city and highway planners – until these can be convinced of the need for a sensible conservation policy, the work and ambitions of the most energetic conservation societies will be brought to nothing.

In my experience, people quite naturally look at things from a purely personal and selfish point of view until some other convincing argument is put to them. It was not so very long ago that we all thought that the different vested interests in the countryside in Britain were wholly incompatible. We all thought that the differences between them and their outlook were so great that nothing could bring them together.

However, the situation was becoming desperate, so we organised a conference and to everybody's amazement there were no rude words, no accusations and no counter-insults. It very soon became apparent that, with a little give and take and a genuine attempt to appreciate and understand the needs of different groups, these apparently widely divergent factions found it possible to agree to co-operate. Without this co-operation every group will suffer by default and the cause of conservation will be irretrievably damaged if not lost altogether. With co-operation and understanding any sacrifices which have to be made are at least in the general interest of conservation as a whole and each interest will get a fair share.

None of this can be entirely free from either emotion or self-interest. The wholesale condemnation of pesticides of all kinds is no more sensible than the indiscriminate use of the argument that the starving millions must be fed. There is a very important place for the proper pesticides properly used. The starving millions must certainly be fed, but the total subjugation of all farming land in the advanced countries to uncompromising chemical and mechanical techniques will not achieve this. We cannot even arrange the distribution of existing surplus production, and not even the most rudimentary of modern methods have filtered through to the vast farming potential of the under-developed countries.

In any case, the whole problem of starving millions in the future would be very considerably reduced if we could begin to control the population explosion.

The manufacturers of pesticides and agricultural equipment do not have a monopoly in concern for the problems of under-nutrition and malnutrition, most people who worry about conservation can also claim the same humanity and compassion. That is not the point, we have got to get the problems and the solutions into the right perspective.

The fact is that for the first time in history Man has got complete control over his habitat. We can, if we so wish, or if we just let things slide, grossly over-populate the earth. We can, if we so wish, pollute the land, the water and the air. We can, if we so wish, exterminate any or all animals which might get in the way of our farms or cities. We can, if we so wish, convert all the jungles and the deserts and the swamps and the mountains into some form of usefully productive land. I daresay we could grow strawberries on the top of Mount Everest if we really tried. We can, if we so wish, cover the whole landscape with concrete to give all the motor-cars a chance to drive about at the same time. If we can do all these things, surely we can decide what sort of habitat we would like to live in first and then make plans and arrangements to achieve it.

I do not aspire to speak for anyone else but I know what sort of habitat I would like to see. First, I would like to see a stabilised world population so that we need make no further demands on land resources. I would like to see farming techniques in all countries developed in sympathy with the needs of wild populations, but to the point where no one need go hungry. I would like to see all land-users show reasonable concern for the consequences of their plans so that mankind's needs for food, power, water, highways and cities can be met without unnecessary or avoidable destruction or dislocation of wild populations and the balance between them.

We have the power to do all these things now, but we cannot do them until more people come to understand what is happening to the world's wildlife and come to see the vision of what the world could be like, and until there exists a general will and determination to get it.

This, in my opinion at least, is where conservation societies can play such a vital part. Perhaps the most encouraging development in recent years is the formation of the World Wildlife Fund, a fully international organisation to which many nations make contributions. The important point is that all these societies should not operate in the narrow sense of trying to keep everything as it was but in the more constructive sense of pointing the way to a better future and helping to create it.

It is not reasonable to expect hard-working farmers or hard-pressed engineers to visualise their activities as part of the broad sweep of human existence automatically. Life is too short, the day-to-day demands and problems are too immediate, and the short-term aims of greater productivity, greater profit and more land under cultivation are more obvious. But this does not mean that they will reject the case for conservation out of hand. They are sensible and intelligent people and they will respond to sensible and intelligent argument. It is up to the conservation societies to make the approaches and to put forward their case moderately but with force and conviction. They have a very good case.

There are many problems and situations which afflict the world over and over again. There will always be poverty and oppression, hunger and lack of opportunity in some corner of the world. There always has been and there always will be. These are recurring problems requiring continuing solutions.

Conservation is dramatically different. It is really a case of now or never. Wildlife, whether in the shape of birds, animals, fish or plants, is being threatened and eroded as never before in history. If we do not get the answer right now, there will not be a second chance, and this, our generation, will go down in history as the people who failed by neglect and indifference to take decisive control of our environment for the benefit of our successors in the future.

Of course we may all be dead by the time the full horror of our neglect becomes apparent, but I for one do not relish the idea of my grandchildren asking me what went wrong.

From an Address to the Canadian Audubon Society,
November 8, 1967

PART III

Machines and Horses

ONE

Helicopters

I MAKE frequent use of helicopters and indeed I very much enjoy flying them myself, but in spite of that I have sadly come to the conclusion that the time has come to ban the helicopter.

In the first place it is manifestly unjust that Concorde alone should be the target of the 'Stop-Everything Brigade'. We are living in an age which seems to believe that we must all sink together because it is undemocratic to swim separately. Therefore I believe that helicopters should stand by Concorde and demand to be banned as well, as a gesture of brotherly solidarity.

Then, the conservation case against helicopters is much the same as the case against Concorde. After all, helicopters use much the same fuel and I daresay if you added up all the fuel used by helicopters all over the world it would probably amount to considerably more than Concordes are likely to use. Then, of course, helicopters are made from more or less the same non-renewable raw materials and, as these are due to run out fairly soon, the ban would only be advancing the inevitable.

As far as pollution is concerned, the situation is really very serious. If you stand as far away as about three feet from a helicopter exhaust there is an overpowering smell of burnt kerosene and a really dreadful noise. This sort of thing is quite intolerable and should obviously be stopped at once. The situation is even worse if the helicopter is airborne because by the time you can hear an approaching helicopter it is close enough to frighten the living daylights out of you.

But these are not the only reasons for the ban. In my view, helicopters are quite obviously socially unjust and, as social justice is the aim and purpose of every enlightened political party, this is a very important factor. After all, in proportion to the total population, only a very few people either own a helicopter or make use of one, therefore no one should take advantage of a helicopter until everybody can have one. It stands to reason.

Helicopters are also commercially extremely unfair. The organisations which use them gain a completely unjustified advantage and if the others are to keep up it would mean a whole new system of subsidies, and naturally the money could not be spared from the subsidies to far more important commodities, which I shall forbear to mention.

One of the most serious considerations is the really appalling effect the use of helicopters has on executives. They save so much time and effort that there is a significant danger that they might be able to accomplish more work and they might even be able to make a bigger profit than their competitors. This is an extremely worrying situation as it implies that these excess profits are made by shamelessly exploiting the consumer. Fortunately, there is every indication that the Treasury is well aware of this immoral practice and has the matter well in hand.

Finally, the manufacture and maintenance of helicopters is industrially unjust and wasteful of manpower. It is quite ridiculous in this day and age that any industry should demand such high standards of skill and craftsmanship. We must get our priorities right in these things. We live in a changing world and we must recognise the changes. In this enlightened and progressive age, in which we are so fortunate to be living, employment must be created which is appropriate to the needs and aspirations of those who are in their wrong minds. It should be obvious to everyone that many more people should be employed in such activities as making porno-graphic films – with ample time off for demonstrating, of course – or in looking after tourists.

If I can persuade you to join me in this campaign the disappearance of the helicopter is assured and then we shall all be able to hold our heads high – as we march steadily back towards the caves our ancestors so foolishly vacated such a long time ago.

TWO

Test Pilot

MY TROUBLE is that I know just enough about flying to realise how little I know about it. However, there is one thing I can say without any worry. Anyone who has flown as a passenger or who has himself flown an aircraft owes more to test pilots than he is ever likely to admit.

I have to confess that I have frequently speculated – like Walter Mitty perhaps – whether I would like to have been a test pilot. I thought it idle to speculate whether I could have been a test pilot – I do not like hypothetical questions. After a little reflection on the subject, I came to the conclusion that a test pilot had an impossible job.

As everyone knows, an aircraft is the end product of a combined effort by research scientist, designer, engineer and manufacturer. There it stands, all bright and shiny and full of theoretical promise. At this point, the test pilot is invited to 'suck it and see'. He is the poor mug who has to discover whether the thing has any aptitude for flight and eventually he has to prove it is safe to fly it. His problem does not end with proving new aircraft, there is always some genius working out improvements and modifications. This strikes me as a positively dangerous occupation and, furthermore, it demands a faith in designers and in the people who put the bits together about as great as a bishop's faith in God. Indeed in this context the bishop has a considerable advantage. After all, most designers have not the least idea how to fly any aeroplane, whereas the bishop has no problem of this sort to worry about. However, bishops and designers have this in common: a bishop can remedy his sins in a confession box while the designer can get rid of his sins in little black boxes.

I suspect that the test pilot's greatest difficulty is that he is, in effect, a critic. It is true that his criticism is intended to be constructive, but still he is a critic and critics are seldom popular.

Aircraft are designed to fly and a great deal of work has to be done before they can be urged to take to the air. At this moment of the designer's triumph, the first instant his brain child shows the least talent for flight, the test pilot has to begin his job of criticism. I would have thought that this was the stuff to strain the firmest friendship. Having reduced the designer to tears, the test pilot has to face the manufacturer who, I would suspect, is not madly keen to hear a list of criticisms, each of which probably adds another half million to his costs and another month's delay to the finished product.

Of course, not all test pilots have to contend with brand-new aircraft but, whether they do or not, both sorts have to face a remarkable fact of engineering life. You can test and check any mechanical device till you are blue in the face and nothing goes wrong, but the moment you put it into the hands of a customer he can be guaranteed to find some obvious weakness within a fortnight.

I am sure that all test pilots have done a course on how to control all sorts of human instincts. I hope so, because without it I know that I would suffer from what might be described as the 'Pride in Responsibility' syndrome. Anyone who has ever tried to breed and train a gun dog or a horse should know the symptoms. It is simply that any defect or weakness becomes a reflection upon your ability to select and train the animal in question and is therefore condoned or ignored. If I got to like an aircraft, I would find it difficult not to excuse some of its weaknesses or, alternatively, I would not like to give it my approval until I was absolutely satisfied, by which time of course the company would be broke.

I cannot help feeling that one of the most difficult problems must be evaluating new systems and innovations. Testing, like any other human experience, is a comparative process and the familiar must always have attractions over the new and the strange. To make objective judgements under these conditions cannot be easy. This desire to cling to the familiar can have very curious results and, when aviation was in its infancy, reactions to this new and strange phenomenon were not always very far-sighted.

For instance, the Secretary of State wrote to A. V. Roe in 1909 to say that the Government 'regretted being unable to help Aviation Pioneers by giving them orders as there was no possibility of ever using aeroplanes for war purposes'. It looks silly in retrospect, but it is a little sobering to think that we may be saying and doing things now which will look just as silly in the future. Equally, of course, things which look extremely silly now may turn out to make a lot of sense.

After all, it must have taken considerable nerve and credulity for the War Office to appoint a Texan ex-buffalo hunter and ex-circus sharpshooter to be Kiting Instructor to the British Army in the early 1900s. It must have looked extremely silly at the time and yet it turned out that Samuel Franklin Cody was a quite remarkable pioneer in aviation with an exceptional flair for cautious testing, careful analysis and ingenious development.

It is quite apparent now that many people thought Barnes Wallis's swing-wing Swallow was silly, but that has also been conveniently forgotten.

In all this conflict of new and old, strange and familiar, and in the confusion of human emotions, the test pilot has somehow got to keep a grip on reality. He has got to find the best and most practical without allowing himself to be held back by doubt or urged on by optimism. He has got to be prepared to be unpopular and, if his reason dictates it, he must be ready to be unfashionable as well. The designer can have faith and enthusiasm, the manufacturer can have conviction and determination, but the test pilot must have common sense.

THREE

Polo

A POLO match begins long before the teams line up on the field of play. This is of course true of many other games that require planning, preparation and training. In polo, however, there seems to be a much wider scope for gamesmanship, skulduggery and temperament in general before the game begins. It is also important to remember that polo is played for fun.

Polo comes somewhere between the standard eleven-a-side field games like football and field hockey and two-man games like tennis. As each player represents a quarter of the strength of the team the problem of filling the place of any drop-out is relatively serious. Furthermore, polo is not exactly cheap and anyone wishing to play must either be well-heeled, have a good job or be supported by an indulgent parent or sponsor. If he happens to be married, his wife needs to be very understanding and long-suffering.

Wives play an extremely important part in polo and many promising young players have had the terrible choice of keeping their ponies or keeping a wife. Some lucky ones somehow manage to persuade their wives to keep, groom and train their ponies, but this ideal arrangement is understandably rare.

But to get back to the cost. People with money are people who can indulge in whims or, if they are still in the business of making money, they are liable to sudden calls to mysterious meetings in Caracas or Hong Kong. Whims can include anything from a week's salmon fishing in Iceland to an African safari or a girl friend in Miami.

The problems, therefore, of getting a team together and keeping it together are formidable and the pre-season negotiations would do credit to any near-eastern carpet vendor.

There are of course many occasions when none of this applies. Regimental and service teams generally; international teams, representative teams and teams travelling abroad are quite different and have problems of equal magnitude but of a different sort. They are better organised and their motivation – if that is the right word – is of a higher order than that of a party of four friends agreeing to play together. Their polo is as much fun but a certain note of earnestness enters into it and things like practising, tactical discussions and the allocation of ponies are taken rather more seriously. They also tend to get angrier with each other during the game.

As the appointed day for the match approaches there are ample opportunities for ponies as well as players to go sick or lame and for all sorts of alarming news to filter through about the unexpected brilliance of the opposition and the threatened romantic excursion of your own best player.

Should, by some remote chance, the team remain intact and in the unlikely event of it having the services of sufficient relatively competent ponies and co-operative grooms,* a certain amount of team practice should be possible. If nothing else, there will be a lot of talk about ponies, tactics and plans, all washed down with suitable refreshment in the club house. Of course the best arrangement is to play with three friends. When this happens the whole season becomes a real joy and every game a pleasure whatever the result.

In the meantime, the psychological warfare continues unabated and, unless the person considering himself more or less responsible for the team (Captain is not exactly the right word for this position except in highly-organised teams) keeps a careful look-out, he may well find that one of the best ponies has been sold just before the big match.

Polo is a social game and some of its most serious hazards are encountered at the parties and entertainments which are such an inevitable feature of all tournaments.

Not many years ago two teams due to meet in the final of an important tournament found themselves invited to attend dances at their respective clubs the night before the match. It was quickly agreed that the Parliamentary system of 'pairing' would solve the problem and all through the evening telephone messages flashed to and fro about the number and condition of the opposition players still attending. In point of general health the two teams were fairly evenly matched the next day, but by the end the strain began to tell, and one unfortunate and experienced player

---

* In England, at any rate, grooms are mostly girls and the majority of them are passionately devoted to the ponies, but their relations with their employers have been known to vary.

committed a foul which under normal circumstances only a beginner would have committed, and the match was won and lost.

You may well believe that after all this pre-match activity the game itself is an anti-climax. Nothing could be further from the truth. Hard-lipped tycoons give every sign of extreme nervousness, elderly players with battered hats and years of experience can be seen to take a nip of something to help them along. False teeth are put away safely and every kind of body protection is fitted into place; sometimes to protect old injuries but more often in anticipation of new ones.

As the teams ride out to the field it all looks splendid: shining ponies glistening in the sun as they glide over the green turf; players doing their best to look unconcerned and as comfortable in their saddles as cowboys, while they make elaborately stylish practice swings. Meanwhile there is much exchanging of pleasantries for the last time with opposition and umpires.

The match then begins and all the previous anxiety and planning, organisation and practice is put to the test in forty minutes of flashing sticks, galloping ponies, curses, bumps, shouts, hits to warm the heart and misses to chill the spine.

Some can do it right away but others require a moment or two before they settle down and remember to get into the right position, look for and cover their opposite number, check where their team mates have got to and what they are doing; look for the ball, recognise a familiar situation and move to anticipate the next development. There is time for a moment of satisfaction as things go your way and the game surges towards the opponents' goal, disappointment as it goes over the back line or elation as it goes through the goal.

The pace can be pretty fast so that any tactical moves must be almost instinctive or they tend to dissipate in the excitement. In club polo it is almost better to know the individual idiosyncrasies of the players on both sides than to attempt a tactical plan. If old 'so and so' has never been known to connect on the near side in his life this can be a very important consideration if there is a cup at stake.

There are moments of awful realisation. The ball is overrun by the rest of the players and there it sits rolling gently to a standstill and all you have to do is to get your pony balanced and going in the right direction. You take a swing – and miss. Fortunately the game goes on and something else happens before you can think of a quick and easy way to commit suicide.

Again, there comes a moment when you have turned a bit late to go back in defence and your opponent looks to be getting away. Fortunately it is the only time you are on a pony that can go faster than a slow trot and you set off in pursuit. You get up to him and by reaching as far forward as possible you just manage to catch the end of his stick as he hits at goal. Clunk, he hits your stick instead and the situation is saved. He looks round, and if looks could kill . . .!

Any player fortunate enough to have one or more good ponies knows that he can concentrate absolutely on the game, his control of his pony is reflex and his pony's actions become immediately extensions of his own. He wants to be there, and in a flash he is there; he wants to whip round, and by some equine gymnastic movement his pony has done it.

On the other hand a bad pony is worse than a penance. It either will not stop or it will only turn one way, or it will neatly side-step just as you are making a shot. It may even stop dead as you are making a particularly beautiful near-side backhander and then only the most experienced riders can avoid an involuntary flight over the pony's head. It will not ride off another pony, and if it sees a pony approaching it slides firmly away and no kicking or beating makes any difference.

If there is anything worse than a bad pony, it is bad weather. Polo should only be played on a smooth hard surface of lawn grass in blazing sun. Unfortunately these conditions cannot be relied upon – certainly not in England. But the tournament must go on, and anyone who has had to play in the third match on a soft ground already badly cut up, in cold drizzling rain, has been through one of life's more unpleasant experiences. Some years ago an important final was played in the rain on a slippery ground. Six of the eight players were on the floor at one time or another and in one spectacular pile-up three were on the ground together. While things were being sorted out one of the players was seen to be resting in a chair thoughtfully provided by a kind spectator. If polo players pray at all – which is not altogether certain – they pray for fine weather for the big match.

The game, as everyone knows, is between two teams but there are additional hazards in the shape of umpires who are supposed to see that the players comply with the rules. These long-suffering citizens may be close friends and boon drinking companions of all the players in normal life, but in a game they become mutton-headed dolts, totally ignorant of the simplest rules of the game and completely blind to monstrous and blatant fouls committed by the opposition. At the same time they seem to take a fiendish delight in blowing the whistle every time you get anywhere near the ball and then rub in the insult by awarding appallingly unfair penalties.

It does happen in some games that everyone is on their best behaviour and the whistle is seldom necessary. These are the best games, with plenty of galloping, no interruptions, exciting for the spectators and no strain on the tempers of the players and, incidentally, a great relief to the umpires.

Just a word about shouting. Polo can be, and usually is, a rather vocal game. Roughly speaking, the noise gets louder as the standard gets worse. Very good polo is played in almost total silence. This is largely due to the fact that good polo is so fast that there is virtually no time to say anything except to give warnings or instructions.

It should also be said that in bad polo there are usually bad ponies and a good deal of the shouting refers to what the rider would like to do to his pony and what he thinks of its ancestry. Shouting, which is neither warning, nor instructional, nor directed at the pony, is more or less without exception abuse. There is really not much venom in it and very frequently it is produced more by fright than by animosity. People have been known to be warned and even sent off for the fluency and volume of their invective, but they are usually the mildest and most cheerful souls off the field. Contrary to what might be supposed, players of the Latin races are less, rather than more, vocal than Anglo-Saxons. However, as their shouting is in a foreign language, it is possible to mistake words of praise for terms of abuse.

The field of play is relatively large and with only eight players it may seem thinly populated; but ponies are heavy creatures and go quite fast so, in spite of the advantage of twice as many legs as we have, collisions and falls are inevitable. They usually happen so quickly that the next thing you know is that you are ploughing a furrow through the turf with your nose or lying gazing at the hospital ceiling. Contrary to popular belief, falls are not simply a matter of falling off an upright pony. This can, and sometimes does, happen to people who want to reach out just a bit too far. On the whole, falls are due to ponies coming down and, naturally, the rider has no option but to go down as well. Some falls can be quite gentle, such as when a pony slides on to the ground. However, when a pony's front legs are tripped while travelling at speed, the rider feels a sensation not unlike an astronaut being launched into space. The only difference is that the rider has time to realise that his landing is going to be considerably more painful.

Falls are not the only hazard. Sticks can cut and bruise, balls can sting, and all other players seem to have extremely knobbly knees, which they delight in boring into your thigh muscles at every opportunity.

And so the contest rages from one end to the other, sometimes fast and thrilling, sometimes slow and frustrating. No two games are quite the same and no two chukkas produce the same situations. Some are slowed down by the ball going out of play, fouls and falls. Others are non-stop gallops with good clear hitting, close marking and riding off between evenly matched teams; these are the moments to cherish and relive years later.

Eventually the bell goes for the end and, elated or dejected, the teams ride off; the winners generous in their sympathy and the losers trying hard to be equally generous in their praise.

Hot, tired and frequently hurting, you make your way back to the pony lines, thank the grooms, pat the ponies which did well and make friends again with the ponies who did not. Then for a shower, a change and, almost the best moment of all, a cooling and refreshing drink with friends and kindred spirits to whom polo is not just a game but the greatest game of all.

Of course, if it were a cup match and you were fortunate enough to win, there is the momentary adulation of the crowd and probably the only admiring glance you are going to get from your wife or girl friend that day.

FOUR

Horses are Horses

IT IS possible, but supremely unlikely, that anyone with even the slightest association with horses has survived the experience without suffering at least a minor accident. In many cases I suspect that one such accident is very often the last, and the end of a promising equestrian career.

Some optimists tend to assume that, once you have learned the lesson that horses bite at one end and kick at the other, there is nothing further to worry about. No such luck, I am afraid. That is only lesson one in a learning process which will go on as long as you are mug enough to continue to associate with horses.

I cannot say that I have carried out a survey of the tender and vulnerable areas of the anatomy of grooms, but I would estimate that a fairly high proportion of them would show a passable impression of a horse's front teeth. Some hazards have even lent their names to certain physical problems. For instance, Ostler's Toe is a well-known condition of the big toe which obviously derives its name from the bloke whose duty it was to hold the leading horses of a carriage and whose feet were therefore vulnerable to a sudden stamp.

The traditional joke about falling off and having to eat breakfast off the mantelpiece merely reflects a very naive appreciation of the hazards of riding. Anyone with experience of the indignity of falling off will confirm that, nine times out of ten, you land on the point of a shoulder, and the most frequent injury is a broken or dislocated collarbone. I can only say that my shoulders would make interesting specimens for any medical school. I say 'indignity' advisedly because the horse is a great leveller and anyone who is concerned about his dignity would be well advised to keep away from horses. Apart from many other embarrassments there is, for instance, no more ridiculous sight than a horse performing its natural functions with someone in full dress uniform mounted on its back. A horse which stops dead just before a jump and thus propels its rider into a graceful arc provides a splendid excuse for general merriment. It has happened to me, but the horse rubbed the joke in by sailing over the jump and me as I lay partly in a ditch on the other side. The devoted horseman learns to put up with this sort of thing but incidents like that can easily sour relations for a bit.

I remember an occasion in Singapore when I had been prevailed upon to play in a polo game. I was always reluctant to play on unknown ponies, but this was considered to be rather unsporting and on this occasion I was persuaded that it would give the local game much encouragement if I took part. Things started badly. The first pony flatly refused to go on to the ground and the spectators, eager with anticipation, were treated to the sight of the star attraction being whizzed around in backward circles until I had to admit defeat.

There is a great and, I feel, unappreciated difference between falling off, falling down and getting off. Falling off simply by reason of not being able to stay on during an unexpected movement of the horse is a major hazard to learners but it tends to decrease with experience. Falling down is inevitable if the horse falls down and it can be both more or less painful than falling off. Years ago I was galloping along in the middle of a game in Malta when the whole thing was suddenly interrupted by my pony disappearing under me. I collected a bruise from hip to ankle on the hard ground and eventually discovered that one of the straps on the protective boots on the front legs of the pony was long enough for the other foot to stand on.

Breaking of equipment frequently causes disasters. On some occasions the only cure for a broken bridle is simply to get off. That sounds all right, but if the pony is travelling at any speed the execution calls for considerable resolution.

Sometimes it takes a moment or two to recognise what has happened. During one game I had the distinct impression that the horse's head was getting further and further away. The mystery was solved when I bit the ground and found that the girth had broken.

Falling down does not always result in anything serious. I once saw an umpire doing a bit of schooling between chukkas with a cigarette in his mouth. The pony fell and nearly rolled over, but it managed to struggle to its feet again and the umpire was still on top and the cigarette was still going.

Some injuries – but not many – do not involve the horse at all. The nearest I ever came to doing the splits was when I caught my knee against the knee of a player going the other way. As a consequence I have a beautiful example of what popular medicine describes as 'Rider's Bones'. These are more usually acquired as a result of small tears in the riding muscles which become hardened and calcified.

I realised it was asking for all kinds of new trouble when I gave up polo and tried my hand at driving. All went well in the first season but that was only beginner's luck. The following year every sort of thing happened. It started when I was doing a bit of water-crossing practice. The water was not quite wide enough and the mud was a bit too soft. As the front wheels sank into the mud the wheelers tried to jump the water and I was catapulted on the end of the reins clear across the water on to the soft bank on the other side. I can still see the look of astonishment on the face of the chap who was left sitting on the box on the other side of the water.

Later that year at Lowther the whole drama of a capsize, as I got a wheel over a stump, was captured by the cameras. Fortunately no great harm was done and as my referee was an ex-point-to-point rider he was not unduly upset, although I suspect he is now an ex-referee as well. The carriage, which was of traditional wood construction, was fairly knocked about and needed almost completely rebuilding. I now have a metal-framed vehicle with metal wheels.

The only moderately serious accident while driving resulted from a broken pole, so now I have a metal pole. It bends, but it has not broken – yet. At one international event I succeeded in breaking three main bars of the swingletree. On the first occasion the grooms were down and chasing the leaders as soon as it happened; but they were a bit surprised that, even having caught their bridles, the horses were reluctant to stop until they looked round and saw that I had been pitched off the box into the heather. I now have a set of metal swingletrees.

Having a family which seems to be equally willing to be humiliated by the horse, I have to live with the expectation that they too will suffer injury and indignity. The only advantage of the personal experience of this sort of thing is that I am not surprised when it happens to them and that I am full of sympathy and useful advice for treatment and recovery.

The trouble with anything to do with horses is that, by the time you have discovered all the problems and risks, it is too late to be of any practical use.

PART IV

Engineering, Technology and Design

ONE

Aeronautics

THE INTERESTING point about today's meeting of the Royal Aeronautical Society is that the hundred years which it celebrates virtually covers the whole story of man's aeronautical activities. Although much thought was given to the problems before that and there were isolated attempts to get into the air, a consecutive series of events only began about a hundred years ago.

Considering the enormous preponderance of heavier-than-air flying machines in use today, it is not altogether surprising that we have come to associate aeronautics exclusively with that particular branch of the art, science, or black magic of getting off the ground.

It comes as quite a surprise to many people to find that the Royal Aeronautical Society was formed almost forty years before the first powered flight. To anyone involved in aeronautics this is of course very stale news but even so it comes as a healthy reminder that some very ambitious and enlightened men were trying hard to get into the air a long time ago. It also says a lot for these early enthusiasts that, unique among similar groups, they formed an Association before rather than after any recognised profession or industry had come into existence. That kind of hopefulness, or perhaps wish-fulfilment, seems to have remained with aeronautical people ever since. How else can one explain the breath-taking impudence of the early long-distance flying feats or the flights of fancy which have given rise to latter-day projects in aeronautical engineering?

There can be no doubt that the foundation of the Royal Aeronautical Society and its subsequent activities have had a profound effect on the development of aviation in this country and to a certain extent all over the world.

It is easy enough to assess the contribution which individuals have made in particular cases and the record of companies and research establishments are there for all to see. The Society's influence on the other hand, is more subtle. It has brought together individuals from all sides of aviation with theories and calculations, arguments and novel ideas and from this exchange the broad pattern of British aviation practice emerges.

Every occupation or profession seems to develop its own group characteristics. I am not going to attempt to describe them but I do not think I am being fanciful by suggesting that farmers on the whole have a different general approach from, say, lawyers or civil engineers. I suppose the simplest explanation would be that certain occupations and professions attract like-minded people, particularly when the motive for joining is more than purely commercial.

This really must be so because if the selection of a career depended solely on commercial considerations I think I am safe in saying that aeronautics would have taken a great deal longer to develop, if indeed it had started at all. More than any other of mankind's occupations, aeronautics has depended upon enthusiasm and utter devotion, bordering on an obsession, to the whole idea of flying. Matched, I might add, by anything ranging from indifference to horror felt by people who are not interested in flying.

Whereas the early days of the railways, for instance, saw a few light-hearted stunts, railway engineering very soon settled down to a severe and practical commercial development. Railways had their steam locomotive fans but only with the recent crop of closures has any public emotion been re-awakened. Aeronautics, on the other hand, owes its very existence to showmanship, stunts, gimmicks and popular wonder and excitement. The whole business was new and mysterious and delightfully dangerous and uncertain. Today railway and shipping companies can order what equipment they like with but a passing flutter of comment or criticism.

Not so in aeronautics, where every bit of equipment for civil or military use is argued with an ignorance almost directly proportional to the emotion provoked and inflamed by righteous indignation about the cost.

The novelty and audacity may have worked off but in their place aeronautics has become spiced with that irresistible element of national prestige and international competition, otherwise reserved almost exclusively to sporting contests. But, even though aeronautics may owe a great deal to showmanship, spectacular stunts and popular excitement, that should never be allowed to obscure the more decisive contribution of rational scientific engineering, solid technical progress and commercial development.

Yet popular interest and inventive engineering alone could not have provided the pressure to bring about the improvement in performance which has since taken place. I do not think anyone could reasonably claim that the present or future standards of airliners were entirely due to spontaneous public clamour.

The determining factor was undoubtedly the military application of aeronautics very early in its existence. Like so many other novel ideas, this happened almost entirely in spite of conventional military thought. It needed the stimulus of actual warfare to make aviation an accepted part of the military establishment. Military – and I include naval – aviation certainly would not have developed at the rate or in the direction it has done without the necessity and practical experience of the two world wars.

Furthermore, the technical progress stimulated by wartime necessity had a profound influence on the subsequent commercial development of aviation. The very novelty of aviation meant that before the First War its military application was entirely speculative and then during the war its development depended upon an arbitrary and pragmatic reaction to events.

The development of military weapons and techniques between wars is always a bit uncertain because the difference between what people think is going to happen in war and what actually happens increases in direct proportion to the interval between wars. It is further complicated by what some people would like to happen in war.

The potential in aviation was so great between the wars that it is not at all surprising that policy decisions about the system for stating require-ments, research and development of designs and manufacture, the creation of an independent air force, the bombs versus battleships excitement, air defence problems, the relative values of tactical and strategic operations, the cost-effectiveness of the bombing campaign, abstract concepts of air power and the practical exploitation of flying machines, have all generated a heat and passion well in keeping with the popular excitement, personal devotion and brilliant engineering which are the hallmark of aviation.

The argument about the use of air power in the Second World War is only just beginning to hot up, while the military application of aviation now, and in the future, is being debated with an abandon previously only experienced in religious arguments, and with about as much chance of a rational outcome. On top of that it is obvious that ordering military equipment abroad is a new and important influence on the development of aviation in this country.

I do not propose to go any further into the development of military aviation for obvious and sufficient reasons, but naturally the demands made by military aviation in the light of the world situation have a very considerable influence on the work done at research establishments and the designs produced by the manufacturers. Even though warfare demanded particular types of aircraft, this development certainly helped to advance the whole art and science of aeronautics.

As the wars receded and designs became more specialised, so the division between military and civil aviation has grown. The very peculiar and special conditions under which civil aviation operates today, and the areas in which competition takes place, have helped to create specialised civil aircraft which are economic within those particular conditions. National prestige, the international control of ticket prices, the control of landing rights and national air space and so on, all tend to modify the purely commercial considerations of manufacturers and operators. But, like so many things, the game has to be played to the rules even if the rules sometimes look a bit odd.

Military and civil passenger aircraft are of course the major components of aviation today but it would be wrong to ignore the tremendous growth of what has come to be known as general aviation. The environment in which general aviation has developed is quite different. For one thing the price of light aircraft is now well within the purchasing power of many individuals in the more prosperous countries. Unlike the big stuff, the use of aircraft in general aviation is influenced to a greater extent by weather conditions, distances, the existence of other means of transport and other very practical considerations. It is quite obvious, for instance, that the potential use of light aircraft in this country will never compare with the larger countries with better weather conditions. As there is little prestige value or technological fall-out to be derived from general aviation, the degree of official encouragement varies very much from country to country. I am sure everyone here knows only too well the conditions which prevail in this country.

Yet the pattern of control and support, and general involvement of Government in the aircraft industry, were set by the special circumstances of war and this has had a decisive influence on the whole evolution of aviation.

If there have been endless discussions about the military and civil applications of aviation, these have only been rivalled by the discussions about the relationship and responsibilities of Government to aviation. This has been reflected in the variety of agencies and ministries which have come and gone in this country in recent years. The recent reports of the Public Accounts Committee also have some bearing on this difficult subject.

No matter how efficient the component parts of Government or an industry may be, how competent the managers or how brilliant the engineers, its general performance is governed by the environment in which it works. The factors which control the aircraft industry, apart from defence, are first the commercial considerations and the relationship between makers and users; second, the method of control and support employed by the Government; and, third, the degree of personal enthusiasm and competence of individuals at all levels in the industry.

There has never yet been any doubt about the degree of personal enthusiasm and competence and, even though Government is deeply involved through its fiscal measures and as the major customer, there is nothing mysterious or special about commercial considerations as related to the aviation industry. This leaves the problem of Government control and support. As this is an extremely touchy subject let me just put it this way. If the relationship between Government and aviation is right and if the system it uses to support the industry and to order military equipment as a whole is the right one, then aviation and the nation will benefit. If the relationship is wrong and if the system of support is applied in the wrong way, all branches of aviation will have to operate under a very severe handicap. It is, of course, easy enough to say what is wrong – it is a great deal more difficult to suggest what would be right.

Now that almost all the basic industries in this country are more or less dependent on Government support in one form or another, and as Government by its purchases for defence is by far the biggest customer of the aviation industry, it would seem about time to make a rational assessment of the principles of applying this support. By support I mean loans, direct subsidies for particular projects, capital write-off, import restrictions, discriminatory taxation and tax relief, development contracts and various methods of assisting exports and partial or outright ownership of manufacturing companies. Every human endeavour is governed by the environment in which it seeks to operate. Subsidy in any form is a very important factor in that environment and it may well be decisive when it comes to planning future developments. In my opinion at least it is much more important to get the environment right than to worry exclusively about future projects.

In retrospect the sequence of discoveries, inventions and applications seems to follow a nice orderly path, as one leads logically to the next. In fact at any given point in time the future is obscure and the next step is nothing like as obvious as it appears after it has been taken. The most remarkable example of this was the hiatus after the Wrights' first success-ful attempt at powered flight. In current jargon this would have been described as a dramatic break-through, but at the time it was strangely ignored.

For many of the early years the progress of aviation was more or less haphazard. Only war necessity and later commercial interest brought some coherence to the selection of projects and the planning of research. On the whole the deliberate selection of the next step probably speeded up progress but there are a good many examples of wrong projects being selected which led to dead ends or very expensive failures. As aviation has developed so has the cost of projects. Once upon a time it did not really matter whether the wrong project was selected and it was still possible to make jokes about 'back to the drawing board'. Today, a wrong selection can destroy great companies with reverberations throughout the national economy. The problem of selection goes right through from research programmes, development projects, commercial contracts to the proper use of equipment.

The problem of making the right selection in research programmes and development projects has become crucial to the whole of aeronautical evolution. Selection is a function of assessment, judgement, imagination and the ability to make decisions. It is a purely human responsibility and there is, unfortunately, no way of making selection automatic.

Selections can eventually turn out to be right or wrong but decisions can be right, wrong or avoided altogether. If there is anything worse than making a wrong decision it is the inability to make a decision at all. Decisions, preferably the right ones, taken at the right time can make all the difference to success. Furthermore, time-wasting and indecision cost a very great deal of money with nothing to show for the expense.

The critical factor is the atmosphere in which the decision-making machinery has to function. If right decisions are rewarded by progress, success and prosperity, people and organisations will be thrown up capable of making these decisions. If, on the other hand, the atmosphere demands that no risks should be taken, that it is more important not to be wrong, then inevitably the machinery of decision-making will be governed by caution and a negative approach and before long it leads to an attitude which says nothing should ever be done for the first time. This latter situation is bound to be fatal in the long run because the only way never to be wrong is to remove the necessity of making any decision at all. You could not be wrong about any aviation project, for instance, if aviation did not exist.

It is a truism that decision-making is the prime function of management. It follows then that, as Government responsibility for various industries increases, so does its management ability become more important. The concept of Government as a purely policy-making and administrative system no longer applies as Government becomes more directly involved in the process of industrial management. In effect, Government becomes a member of the Board of Directors and this means that Government needs all the specialist management, technological and factual experience which industry has found necessary in order to make the right decisions. This experience is also necessary to give the industries, for which Government has acquired particular responsibilities, the feeling that the decisions are being taken for the right practical reasons and from a position of knowledge. It is probably easier to get a solution to this problem in a wholly free economy, or in a wholly controlled economy, than it is to find a workable answer in an economy which is partly free and partly controlled. There is probably much to be learnt from a comparison of the methods employed in other countries.

Whatever the purely commercial results may have been, aviation has led the field in scientific and technological progress and it has probably been the most important single cause of technical advance in industry as a whole. Quite apart from introducing novel methods of construction and manufacture it has brought into being the whole vast business now called avionics whose techniques have found their way into almost every branch of industry. No one can pretend that the commercial returns of aviation have been spectacular, yet it has attracted probably the best brains in all departments of technology. Unless we are prepared to accept that our best is not good enough we must look elsewhere for an explanation of the industry's problems.

The fact is that not all industrial undertakings operate in exactly the same environment. Mining, for example, has problems which do not exist in the boot and shoe industry. Similarly, aviation occupies a totally different position, within the economy and as a commercial undertaking, from the motor industry. Lumping them all together, however convenient or philosophically satisfying, cannot result in getting the best out of each of them.

The tremendous practical advantages of aviation for long-distance passenger travel and for so many defence purposes has resulted in the rapid growth of the industry and an even more rapid growth in the cost of successive generations of aircraft. The Government has, of course, always been involved as the sole purchaser of defence equipment and also because so much aviation constitutes a civil social service which needs to be regulated by public authority. Few major aircraft in recent years have cost less than £250 million to produce and the next generation looks as if they are going to cost twice as much. To make economic sense the research and development costs should represent something less than 50 per cent of the total costs. In the normal course of events the profits from past successes are used to pay for future projects. For this to happen in the aviation industry would mean an accumulation of profits which, even if possible, public opinion would be bound to feel was excessive. Yet we all believe that it is ridiculous for a country which is supposed to be well advanced in engineering technology, to admit that it cannot cope with aeronautics – the most advanced technology of them all. It is partly for this reason that Government is prepared to use taxpayers' money to support the industry but it is also partly because of the glamour of aviation which makes people prepared to risk more resources in the development of aircraft rather than in other forms of transport, for instance in railways.

For European countries the total investment necessary to achieve success has become so great that individual countries are finding the risks a bit daunting. Out of this has grown the beginnings of international co-operation. It is the obvious answer and technically it has been surprisingly successful, but the system of official co-operation and decision-making still seems to be a bit vague. If it is important to see that aviation is fitted into the national economy in such a way as to enable it to function most efficiently, it is even more important to work out an international structure which will enhance and encourage the chances of success, rather than frustrate and defeat them. One major difficulty is that the development and manufacture of aircraft is a very long-term business which means that decisions have to be taken well in advance. Political government by its very nature is inclined to be short-term and a state of political stability and economic certainty do not always coincide in the different countries concerned.

It is not as if international industrial co-operation is something new or experimental. Several of the largest companies operating in this country have been international for many years. The aviation industry is rather a special case because inter-government co-operation must also take place if it is to meet with any long-term success.

One of the features of aviation is the vast range of potential developments which it contains. Railways and ships, for instance, can be used in a number of different ways but there are certain well-defined limitations. Apart from refinements in control and operation they have reached the end of their practical development. There are practically no such limitations in aviation as yet. Development has always depended upon imaginative projects and imagination in the exploitation of new ideas. The most important factor is the correct use of a new development, not necessarily as an alternative to an existing system, but as an entirely original concept, which has never previously been possible at all. Helicopters are quickly finding their proper use but air cushion vehicles are still only on the fringe. As much depends upon imagination in the use of novel equipment as it does on its invention and design.

In this assessment of the influences on the development of aviation I have made no reference to astronautics. It is true that it has grown out of aeronautics but it has really become an entirely separate subject with its own possibilities, limitations and problems and with its own different reasons for development. In spite of the tremendous public interest in human space flight and the possibility of a man landing on the moon, it all seems rather remote and technological. Aviation is within the grasp and imagination of the average man, it has become part of our human environment. Space activity is more like a gigantic scientific experiment to be admired or to be encouraged for its practical benefits, but difficult to bring within the bounds of human experience. I might add that it is also fairly difficult to bring the scale of costs within human comprehension. This alone means that dabbling in space without a coherent programme or a rational system of supervision wastes a great deal of money with virtually nothing to show for it.

Anyone who knows the facts of aeronautical history and has the time and inclination to analyse them can advance his own ideas of their significance. This brief review just happens to be the way I choose to interpret the facts. I find that aviation as a human activity has certain highly individual characteristics. It is as much an enthusiasm as a scientific, technological or commercial undertaking. More than any other activity it has always depended upon the personal contribution of gifted and far-sighted individuals. Its development has been decisively influenced by historical events and it has grown up with, rather than before, the progressive involvement of Government in industrial activities.

Aviation is not comparable with the straightforward manufacturing industries. All its projects require massive speculative investment and special arrangements have to be made in all economic systems: free, partially free or wholly controlled. The most important of these special arrangements include the system of applying Government support, the relationship with Government for the purpose of organising research, the selection of civil and defence projects and the arrangements for their design and manufacture.

The cost and effort required to maintain a viable aviation industry are so great that international co-operation is almost essential. The administrative arrangements necessary to achieve effective international co-operation are even more important than the internal and purely national arrangements.

Intuition and imagination have always played a most important part in aviation; without them further progress is virtually impossible. However, they cannot ensure success on their own and they cannot begin to operate at all unless the whole system has a thoroughly rational basis.

The first hundred years of aviation have seen some spectacular developments but I do not believe even these will compare with the development in aeronautics and astronautics during the next hundred years. There are formidable problems to overcome, there are any number of possibilities waiting to be exploited and the challenge of space is the most exciting and daunting which mankind has ever faced.

From the Centenary Address to the
Royal Aeronautical Society,
London, September 12, 1966

TWO

Fuel Technology

VARIATION IN diet depends upon several factors: the raw foods available, the general climatic circumstances, the technical equipment for cooking and the skill of the cook. Modern technology depends upon the materials available, the standard of existence of the community and its climatic circumstances, the industrial organisation and the skill of the scientists and technologists. In the case of the development neither of food nor of technology has there been a consistent attempt to look for a need and then to set out to supply it. Most modern technology, like cookery, is the result of detailed improvements to age-old techniques. The whole of the complicated technology of domestic heat, light and power derives directly from primitive wood fires and oil lamps. It is not as if someone had sat down and decided that it would be extremely convenient to have a method of heating or lighting a house. It has been a matter of improving the technique.

Of course there are a number of technological developments which owe their entire existence to the original discovery of scientific facts, but here again it was the haphazard discovery of the facts which allowed the development to take place and not the other way round. By that I mean that, in general, scientific discovery has not been prompted by any particular need, except perhaps to gratify human curiosity.

This is a broad generalisation and I can think of several instances which might tend to prove the opposite but the point I am getting at is simply this: We have now reached a stage in human development where our future technological progress must be based to an increasing degree on the rational needs of our civilisation rather than let our civilisation be driven about aimlessly by haphazard invention.

The difficulty is that before we can make any deliberate attempt to control our future technological development we must have a much better idea of human needs in such things as housing and education, recreation and travel, at work and in the general structure of society. We must know these needs as facts and not as conjectures. We must come to terms with human nature even if it does not fit a conveniently logical theory.

We have much to learn from Konrad Lorenz's studies of animal behaviour. The old Adam in us does not die quite so easily as the Church would like. This may sound unappetising to those people who cherish the romantic notion that all invention and all technology are strictly in the very best interests of mankind and the basis of a new Golden Age. Science and technology have brought untold benefits and enormous wealth, but not without a price.

Few people saw anything but good deriving from the technological and industrial changes of the eighteenth and nineteenth centuries. It was only later that the slums and the slag-heaps became hideously apparent. We are still trying to repair the damage of that industrial revolution. Few events in history can have produced so much poverty and human misery; the legacy of its industrial housing is still with us and the acres of country which it destroyed are only now beginning to be reclaimed.

Yet I get the impression that indiscriminate industrialisation is looked upon as an essential process for all countries, in spite of the fact that we are still uncertain how to avoid its worst effects. As Sir Solly Zuckerman put it recently: 'The world is clearly living through a period in which the aims of politics and the outcome of scientific endeavour appear to clash!'

The immediate difficulty is that no one really knows enough about what constitutes rational human needs. It is easy enough to say what an ideal diet should be but I doubt very much whether anyone would actually enjoy the experience. It is so easy to pontificate about the needs of people; to decide in the abstract what is good for them and then to design an environment which in practice turns out to be much less acceptable than supposed. This is not necessarily due to the cussedness of people, it is just as likely to be due to a lack of understanding of human behaviour.

At all costs we must avoid the situation where a group of people are in a position to dictate what the next man shall want. The problem is twofold: to find out by a process of enquiry and observation what people in general want, and secondly whether or not it can be provided from the resources available. This is not as simple as it sounds; what makes people happy and contented in practice is not necessarily what they say they need to make them happy and contented.

There are currently any number of misconceptions, or at least arguable conceptions which have almost assumed the proportions of holy dogma. Let me give you one or two examples. It is currently fashionable to equate leisure with shorter working hours, whereas it could equally well be argued that leisure is a factor of income and a factor of personal inclination. Idle people may accept the extra leisure which shorter working hours produce but many others use the extra hours available to earn more income by taking another job. In any case shorter daily or weekly hours of work do not necessarily produce leisure time in the most convenient form. Top management, for instance, works long daily and weekly hours but takes its leisure as and when convenient. The higher income means that leisure becomes available in a more acceptable form. I am speculating but I am sure the true situation could be discovered by observation and enquiry.

Take another example. It is held that people always spend the same proportion of their income on their homes. Out of this concept has arisen the questionable system of housing estates development on the basis of income groups. Surely, housing is very much a matter of personal choice. Some people may restrict their outgoings on housing so that they can spend more on something else. Others may have to spend more on housing because of bigger families or merely because they prefer better conditions. Different housing standards are needed at different points of the life cycle. The bland assumption, that people in the same income group want to live together, seems nonsensical in theory and a deliberate creation of class differences when put into practice. Again, I suspect that decisions such as this have been arrived at without sufficient knowledge and understanding.

Then again there is the fear that automation and computer control will lead to loss of work and loss of human initiative. In fact, improving efficiency in production has never led to an overall loss of work. Work is lost by out-of-date methods of production, by a failure to respond to competition. It can just as well be argued that automation and computer-control liberate individuals from massive and monotonous drudgery; allow the same work force to produce more for higher pay; and allow personal thought and inclinations to develop. Technology in this sense is the foundation of a higher standard of human civilisation and presents a prospect of real individual freedom. What people do with this freedom is another matter.

These points may not be very important in a community which has grown accustomed to a rapidly-changing environment. The dangers of making a wrong assessment are far greater when modern technological methods and ideas are introduced to a relatively primitive community. Without a proper understanding of the structure and concepts of such a community, any innovation can cause untold harm and dislocation.

For example, even in Britain it would not be difficult to show that a wrong assessment of the components in our future energy balance could have far-reaching results to our economy and to the lives of many individuals. For instance, if the coal industry were to decline too rapidly it would make the social resettlement of a sizeable population a very difficult and expensive business. Equally, an uncontrolled development of nuclear power might bring in its wake unforeseen contamination problems.

Even where the purely technical development of various forms of fuel and energy causes no particular problems, the administrative, tax and price structure may easily give rise to unexpected and unwanted changes in community existence. For instance, no amount of technical improvement to our transport system will encourage manufacturing industries to develop away from the main centres of population if freight charges, pilfering, delivery delays, and other non-technical considerations make it more advantageous to set up near the source of materials and near the major markets. The introduction of container services and fast freight liners may prove a most important turning point in the whole of the history of freight transport.

In the same way that technical considerations are not the only factors in a technological operation, technology may have much to offer to activities with which it is not usually associated. One very rational human need is the acquisition of knowledge through education, and the opportunities for technology in education are virtually unlimited. Audio-visual tapes for remote communities, literacy programmes transmitted through satellites, teaching machines of various kinds, experience simulators and a whole array of other possibilities are waiting to be developed and exploited.

The ultimate beneficiary of the whole complex of modern technology is the home and the individual within it. In the end, fuel has to be convertible into heat, light and power for domestic use. There are several approaches to this problem. You can have a separate and specialised fuel for each of the three requirements which are independently convertible in the home. At the other extreme you can have the 'Total Energy' concept with one communal source of energy which is convertible within the home and the block of flats into the three requirements. In between there are all sorts of permutations but I doubt whether we have exhausted the possibilities or even found the most convenient arrangement.

For instance, some people like to cook and heat their houses with gas. This means that gas as well as electricity has to be laid on because light and power are provided by that means. The alternative might be a system of light and power operated by gas or perhaps to instal a conversion machine, say a small gas turbine, or fuel cell, which would produce the necessary electricity for light and power, and the waste heat could warm the house. In some areas, although this is doubtful in Britain, solar energy might provide a completely independent source of heat and light and power.

The principle of an individual conversion unit has long been the accepted means of producing hot water and in some cases central heating. But for big centres of population the logical development is large-scale district heating, using ordinary domestic waste as part of the source of fuel. In the same way, sewage can be used as a source of power for its own disposal. Unless technology can provide these facilities equally conveniently for small towns and villages, both in the industrial as well as in the less developed countries, it means that the patterns of human existence will have to undergo radical modification and not necessarily for the better.

It might very well be argued that the tremendous concentration of human population in big cities at the expense of small towns and villages, which has taken place in recent years, is largely due to the fact that domestic facilities such as heat, light, power, water and drains, are more easily provided in big cities. These huge cities are in fact creations of our technology rather than a reflection of human inclination.

Electricity is probably the most convenient and flexible source of domestic and industrial energy but that fact has meant the construction of a vast distribution system, most of which is above ground in the form of wires and pylons. This may provide a satisfactory technological solution but it is also extremely unsightly. We do not get much view of the open sky in this country and when the mists clear it is somewhat discouraging to find the air festooned with towers and wires. In this instance, the distribution of gas, oil and water by underground pipeline is a far more satisfactory arrangement. Research directed at the transmission of electricity underground (perhaps laid in water mains) is an excellent example of technology in the service of a known human need.

This whole division between a central or communal source of supply on the one hand and the provision of separate and independent sources of energy on the other applies in many other fields. In transport, for instance, the railways make use of both systems but other forms of personal and public transport only use the independent source system. Considering the proportions of present-day commuter traffic and the pattern which is developing, there might well be an argument to make both systems available to personal transport.

The advantage of personal transport is that it moves you from A to B without your having to get out and change methods of transport. Yet, for a great part of its route it is following a communal track. Its independence is in fact only valuable at the extremities of its journey. It might be that the ability to attach itself to some form of communal power and direction system might speed the journey time, cut down accidents and generally provide a more efficient transport system and a better fuel/power equation. Perhaps an electric car with rechargeable batteries might lend itself more readily to this kind of operation as it would make it easier to plug in and unplug from some kind of communal monorail. The ideal might be some form of – to use a hideous word – personalised container system on conveyor belts between the home and place of work.

The whole area of public transport is wide open to improvement for commuter services for movement within cities as well as for use in country districts. Computer-controlled spiral rail, monorail or hover-rail systems powered by an electro-magnetic induction system are technical possibilities, but no system will work which does not spring from a sound understanding of the needs of the people.

As it is, modern transport technology has produced a situation where the whole of our urban development is being conditioned by the needs of the existing transport systems. It is no longer a question of how we want to live, it is a question of how to get to and from work, to and from the shopping centres and places of entertainment. A very considerable part of our environment is being dictated by the haphazard demands of current methods of transport. These in turn are dependent upon particular forms of motive power.

Many people have visualised some forms of personal lifting and flying device for short-distance movements. Although this depends upon a satisfactory source of independent energy, the real difficulty about transport through the air is the system of control; there is no point of reference and it is seriously affected by weather conditions. We have certainly neither achieved nor even specified the ideal system of long-distance travel. The main ingredient, the fast big passenger jet, is coming along nicely but the process of getting from door to terminal and terminal to door is a long-winded and uncomfortable process. Furthermore, aviation technology is beginning to make almost unreasonable demands for its terminal installations. If you come to think of it, all present and any future systems of transport depend for their success largely on the cost of their sources of energy. Therefore, having eventually found a system of transport which meets the needs of those who are to use it, its development will depend very much on the efficiency of its source of motive power and the fuel it uses.

It is very easy to fall into the comfortable way of thinking that the present way of doing things is the best and that it will last. The present generation of air-breathing internal combustion engines, for instance, is a major source of air pollution which will get a great deal worse. I do not suppose anyone bothered about air pollution when a coal fire was the ordinary means of heating and cooking, but today there are large areas of smokeless zones because other systems exist. I see that similar restrictions are already being placed on petrol and diesel engines in the United States. This ought to provide a good deal of food for thought.

The lack of control over our technological development shows itself in several ways. Without in any way detracting from the very considerable and important developments which have been pioneered in this country, I think it is quite fair to look at some of the gaps. Britain was one of the pioneers of light aircraft but the light aircraft industry nearly disappeared and there are no modern British light aircraft engines except for a small experimental gas-turbine.

There are some outstanding British-designed diesel-engined railway locomotives but it is surprising how many of these engines are designed abroad and built under licence in this country. The same applies to marine diesels.

The hovercraft industry is going ahead reasonably well but there is only one fairly modern helicopter currently in use which was designed in this country. This means that the Services have to buy this relatively simple piece of technological equipment from abroad.

Perhaps the most serious case of runaway technology is in defence equipment. Each Service in turn has suffered from technological escalation. The Navy lost a carrier, the Royal Air Force lost the T.S.R. 11 and the Army more or less lost a tank. Technology makes it possible to design bigger and better equipment but at a completely unacceptable cost. Furthermore, when the unit cost gets above a certain level, the risk of losing it in action is out of all proportion to its military advantage.

I suppose industry is the main consumer of fuel of all sorts, mostly as a source of power for its production machines. In fact it could be argued that the whole development of factories as we know them is due to the form in which power for production purposes first became available. The big steam engines could only transmit their power through shafts and belts with the result that production machines had to be concentrated near the source of power. This reversed the previous system of production where people did their work in their homes and the raw and finished materials were made to travel.

The factory system is still with us today although it is quite unnecessary except in very particular instances such as ship-building or where there is an economic advantage in large-scale machinery, which needs to be operated round the clock, and of course the final assembly of large products. As it is, the problem of transporting people at peak hours to and from their production machines gets steadily more expensive and more difficult. Whereas, of course, if people could do their work in workshops, attached to their homes or in small local communal workshops, the transport system would only have to contend with the movement of materials at any time of the day or night which proved convenient.

It would have the further advantage that individuals could choose at what time of the day or night they wished to do their work. After all, it is not particularly significant to an employer where or when the work is carried out. In fact, much sub-contracting goes to small workshops as it is: an altogether more flexible and civilised system. However, I am sure there are all sorts of practical objections. It is curious how easy it is to justify any existing system and to find objections to any alternative ideas.

I think it is fair to say that the types of fuel and the methods of converting them into useful and useable sources of energy have had a most important influence on the way in which human life in this techno- logical age has developed. But the point is that our way of life has been influenced by the way technology has developed. In future, it seems to me, we ought to try to reverse this and so develop our technology that it meets the needs of the sort of life we wish to lead and so to adapt it that its impact, especially on the emerging nations, is not unnecessarily disruptive.

For instance, we are only slowly beginning to recognise that the development of farming machinery of all kinds, based on an independent source of power in the form of the internal combustion engine, has completely changed the pattern of country life. We have allowed technology to make it increasingly difficult for the relatively small owner-occupier farmer to make ends meet. Yet, many laws of inheritance and taxation tend to keep properties small. We have transformed farming into an industrial operation where size and turnover alone make it possible to invest in the expensive overheads and capital equipment.

This may be the right way to do it from the point of view of efficient production but to force this pattern on the closely settled agricultural communities of the Eastern world would mean a most tremendous upheaval in their way of life and an almost insuperable problem in sorting out ancient systems of landholding and inheritance. I suppose this could be done by forcing collective farming techniques on these people but I think a more humane solution is to adapt our technology to their needs and to their environment. This would mean the development of small, cheap machines for individual farmers and deliberately designed equipment for produce collection, processing and marketing.

Some changes in the traditional marketing system are inevitable but this is probably best done through a much wider development of farmers' co-operatives, both for purchasing supplies of such things as seeds and fertilisers and for marketing the produce. Where these co-operatives exist, such as in India or in the Gezira cotton scheme in the Sudan, they have been conspicuously successful.

One of the great dangers of using the expressions 'Have and Have-Not Countries' or 'Under-Developed Country' is that they grossly over-simplify an extremely complicated and difficult situation. It is quite unrealistic to suggest that the difference between countries and their standard of existence can be measured by a comparison of their technological equipment. Furthermore, it suggests that the standards of the richest sector of the United States are necessarily desirable, suitable or even attainable by all other countries and communities.

The point seems to be that it should not be necessary to disrupt what has proved to be a reasonably satisfactory human structure merely so as to take advantage of modern technology. The important aim is to raise standards of living and to release the poor from a subsistence farming level of existence.

The vexed question in this theory is that big farms, properly managed, are inevitably more efficient than smallholdings, yet the antipathy to large properties remains just as strong. The fact is that in the industrialised countries farming has become an industry with the land as its workshop. In this connection the reforms which have been carried through in parts of the Near East within the last few years are extremely interesting. Existing cultivated land has been redistributed and the owners of uncultivated land have been given inducements to bring large new areas into cultivation. This means that the area is going to need the most sophisticated agricultural machinery and techniques in order to bring these large areas into production. In addition it will need suitable machinery for the smaller farmers so that they can continue as independent producers at a reasonable level of efficiency.

On the subject of bringing new areas into agricultural production, it is true that modern machinery has made it possible to displace the jungle and drain swamps, but these are the last remaining areas which can sustain wildlife in any quantity. They may be the easiest and most obvious areas to bring into production but it can only be done at the cost of destroying creatures who have had every right to share this planet with us for a long time and should continue to do so. The areas we should be looking at are the deserts, both natural and man-made. The challenge to technology may be greater but in the long run their reclamation will do less harm to our general environment, and more good to our general existence.

Another area where technology is driving instead of being driven is in the oceans. Methods of fishing are becoming more and more efficient but the whole fishing industry is based on the exploitation of a wild population. This is almost a prehistoric concept on land, but it has never been questioned at sea.

The efforts of technologists and legislators ought to be concentrated on systems equivalent to sowing and controlled harvesting ashore. The present free-for-all system is thoroughly destructive and quite apart from anything else it is causing the extermination of the whale, the world's largest and most inoffensive creature. I do not believe the idea of farming whales is really so far-fetched.

The general attitude to the oceans is reflected in their use as a gigantic rubbish tip and the final resting place of the radio-active waste from nuclear fuel. In order that a proper system of oceanic cultivation can be brought into existence a whole new range of technologies will have to be developed. In other words, we must decide that this is the need and then direct technological development in that direction.

If anyone thinks that this is all rather fanciful, let me just say that the whole of space technology has developed either because of its military potential or for the almost inadequate reason that space, the moon and the stars are there. This is technology driving with a vengeance. Mind you, I do not want to establish the idea that I do not think space technology is worth developing; I only want to make the point that the reason for developing technologies for the reclamation of deserts and an orderly harvesting of the seas is no more far-fetched than the reason for developing a vastly expensive space technology.

In the development of any new technology one of the controlling factors is the provision of various forms of energy and power as and when they are needed. I would go further than that. Obviously the greatest effort in fuel technology will always be devoted to the improvement of fuels for sources of energy at present in use, but another part of it will be devoted to fundamental research. My contention is that this fundamental research should be further sub-divided. One part should certainly continue on the basis of curiosity, but the other part should be directed to deliberate technological development.

I fully realise that there is a growing concern for what is described as 'Scientific Policy'. The number and variety of scientific policy and advisory committees in this country alone is fairly impressive. I suspect, however, that in general they are more concerned with the health, progress and money available to the particular discipline with which they are concerned, than with the direction of its efforts in relation to human needs.

I suspect also that the accumulation of statistics has tended to take the place of judgement and management. The national scientific and tech-nological effort is equated with the number of graduates or with the percentage of the G.N.P. devoted to research and development. Efficient use of resources, competent management, an effective structure of responsibilities, quick, reliable and well-informed decision-making: these are even more important but they cannot be reduced to statistics.

Technology marches on but it leaves in its wake polluted seas and rivers, polluted air, polluted land and polluted food. I do not think it is fanciful to suggest that the birds and animals and fish which are dying in this process are equivalent to the miner's canary: the first warning that things are not quite right. Technology undoubtedly produces wealth which gives people more leisure but at the same time it destroys the very places where life and leisure can be enjoyed; all in the sacred name of progress.

At the moment our best thinking power is devoted either to discovery of new facts or to the design of complicated structures and equipment. In the future a great deal more technological thinking power must also be used to give discovery and design a rational direction. We know the tactics of technology; we need to develop the strategy as well. We must get away from the situation where things are made merely because it is possible to make them. Marketable technology should not be the sole justification for research. In its place we must try to achieve the situation where things are made because they can make a valuable contribution to human civilisation. This sort of progress will involve all the technologies working in concert.

Progress is not just being faster and noisier and bigger, progress is to do with people and the environment in which they live. Progress is not simply a matter of new invention, progress means filling ordinary human needs.

There is an old story about three stonemasons who were working on a mediaeval cathedral. When they were asked what they were doing, one said he was earning his living; the second one said that he was cutting a stone to some exact dimensions; the third one said that he was building a cathedral.

I think there is a moral for technology there.

From the Melchett Lecture, the Institute of Fuel,
London, May 23, 1967

THREE

In Praise of Applied Science

IT HAS now become a platitude to say that we live in a technological society, but, platitude or not, this is a fact and we have got to face the consequences. The consequences are roughly these. We have got to train people to service the existing technological equipment at present in use throughout every branch of our domestic, industrial and commercial life. That is the first necessity; the next is to find and train people to develop better and cheaper techniques in all these fields.

The urgent need for this is becoming daily more obvious. Evidence from manufacturers all over the country shows that many parts of the infra-structure of industrial production are not improving their efficiency in comparison with other countries. This infra-structure may not be directly involved but it has an immediate effect on our competition for export markets.

The second platitude is to say that the nation as a whole must run a profitable trading account with the rest of the world. We have got to balance the outflow of payments for raw materials, food and manufactured goods, which we buy from other countries, against the inflow of payments from abroad in return for our exports and services.

We are not alone in this. We have no monopoly of markets overseas. No one is obliged to buy British goods and no one is likely to want our goods and services just because we think we are thoroughly nice, honest and decent people. Our goods and our services have got to compete with those of some very accomplished, energetic and competent people living in other countries.

In this competition we can only win if we produce and market our goods and services more efficiently, if they are better designed, more reliable and preferably cheaper. To do this we must have really professional managers and as many well-trained, imaginative and enthusiastic technologists as we can possibly find. Without them, old industries cannot improve, new industries cannot be developed, neither can become more productive, our trading account will get worse and the whole elaborate structure of our humane and civilised nation will go into a gradual decline.

We are trying to build up in this country a system of human life which is beginning to give all our citizens possibilities undreamed of by our ancestors. But this has to be paid for, and every now and then we should tear ourselves away from the, doubtless fascinating, discussions about how to spend money and concentrate for a bit on the much more complicated problem of how to make it.

The third platitude is that technology is creative and demands a very special talent. Discovery and invention must come first, but the application of ideas and techniques to the needs and comfort of mankind can only be done by people with vision and imagination combined with a professional competence of the highest order.

Sadly, it seems that this message is not getting through to the younger generation. I find it very difficult to escape the conclusion that the responsibility for this rests squarely with the educational system as a whole and of course with parents and teachers.

The number of applied science places of all kinds which need to be filled every year is based on some hard-headed estimates of the needs of the Government, the nationalised, service and manufacturing industries, and of commerce and management, in the years ahead. Contrary to a widely-held belief, these estimates do not include any plans to export the graduates at the end of their courses.

I have attempted to review some of the factors which need to be taken into account when discussing the number of young people who should be given the opportunity to study applied science and the importance of their doing so. We have now to face the facts that not enough are coming forward and the situation is extremely serious.

The first question to ask is, 'Why?' Why is it that young people queue up for arts courses and pure science courses but shun the applied sciences? The answers are bound to be largely conjecture, because even if you were to conduct a poll among young people I am doubtful if they could put their reasons into so many words. It is always difficult to explain why you did not do something.

All I can do is to offer my own conjectures and I can only claim that they are based on a wide but superficial experience with little hard knowledge. I am not suggesting that the order I have put them in indicates any order of priority, the importance of each factor varies with every individual.

Right away I am up against that awful conundrum: 'Which came first, the chicken or the egg?' Is the present content of the science courses in schools due to the fact that teachers of science themselves studied pure science? Or are the teachers of science in schools mostly pure scientists because of the courses they have to teach? Whichever it is, the net result is almost invariably that basic science is taught in schools in preference to any form of applied science.

Added to this is the strongly-held view among many applied scientists themselves that a basic science course is an essential prerequisite to the study of any of the applied sciences.

So far so good, but the situation arises that, if only basic science is taught by teachers who themselves are pure scientists without applied science or industrial science experience, then naturally only those young people who are by nature more interested in pure science will be attracted by and successful in school science courses. The others will look elsewhere.

A recently published report on 'Engineering among the Schools' puts it this way: 'Engineers and the schools are much closer than many of both of them suspect. This fact is obscured by the straight science and mathematics fixation of traditional science schooling.'

Further on it makes an interesting comment on what it describes as 'the triangle of school/examining board/university': 'The schools, it seems, are saying that they have to take straight science and maths because those are the only subjects the universities want; the universities are saying they have to ask for science and mathematics because those are the only 'A' levels available; and some at least of the examining board are saying there is no need to develop new engineering or applied science 'A' levels because the schools and universities are clearly satisfied with what they have.'

I rather doubt whether young people take up particular courses at school merely because of inclination, opportunity or careers advice. There must be more to it than that. One factor must be, for want of a better description, the emotional incentive, which is so obvious, for example, in the choice of medicine, teaching or the Church. These are very deeply rooted, and anyway the so-called 'social' value of these professions has always been immediately and glaringly apparent. Applied science, except in the very primitive sense, is a veritable newcomer on the scene and, because so much of the end product of technology is severely practical, its social value is inclined to be overlooked. Result: no emotional incentive to become an applied scientist.

The fact of the matter is that the 'social value' of applied science is at least as great as in any other profession or occupation and the responsibility for making this crystal clear lies firmly with the teaching profession, aided and abetted by the applied scientists themselves.

Another obvious factor in the choice of a career must be the material attractions of a particular occupation. Business and commerce, for instance, hold out the hope of instant wealth for the minimum effort. (It is not quite like that in practice but folklore seldom gets things exactly right.) By material attractions I mean the salary or money prospects, the opportunity to take part in developing technologies, the hope of achieving standing and respect in the community, the chances of advancement to positions of responsibility and authority, and finally the rewards for hard work and success.

I am sorry to say that a dispassionate look at the modern scene is enough to show that, as far as applied scientists are concerned, the material attractions hardly appear to be sufficient to encourage young people to choose applied science in face of the organisational difficulties at school or the counter-attractions of other occupations. This is also partly due to the fact that many of the material attractions which already exist are not sufficiently known. There is an increasing flow of technologists into senior management, and the exporting industries are increasingly recognising the value of technologists in gaining contracts and in the process of marketing complicated technological equipment.

As long ago as 1963 the then Federation of British Industries appreciated the seriousness of the situation. At that time only 36 per cent of all science and technology students went into industry compared with 68 per cent for West Germany and 49 per cent in the United States of America. Out of this arose the Universities and Industry Joint Committee which was an important step in the right direction. It is generally accepted that the processes of modern industry can only be organised by professional technologists, but until schools, universities, professional institutions and management organisations adjust themselves to this situation, we shall never get the right kind of replacement for the high standard of talent which industrial management enjoys today.

An export drive is necessary so that the nation as a whole can show a profit in its dealings with the rest of the world. In the same way companies, services and industries must show a profit and it is quite pointless to attempt to export unless there is a reasonable chance of making a profit. Exporting is hard work, demanding very high professional and managerial standards and an absolute requirement for drive and efficiency. Exporting should bring its rewards in profits, in the general development and expansion of business and in a personal sense of achievement. It is not subsidies which are needed but rewards for success. It is not fine words and exhortations that are needed but a better set of rules for the game.

It would be a major national disaster if exporters ever began to feel a sense of frustration or discouragement. Exporting is a gamble and the essence of any gamble is the chance to win. I have no objection to someone scooping the pool as a result of marking a card with a lot of crosses, but I cannot help thinking that someone who hits the jackpot in an export market should have the same advantages.

I want to make one more general point. We are all in this unpleasant soup together. The adverse balance of payments is a national problem. It has never been any good saying 'I'm all right Jack – this is somebody else's problem', and in the present circumstances it is completely destructive. It is no good each group or interest trying to pin the blame for any lack of success on some other group. None of us has a monopoly of all the virtues, however much we like to think so.

It is no use the Unions blaming management, or manufacturers blaming civil servants, or both blaming the politicians. We are all about equally competent or incompetent (although of course, circumstances may make us more or less effective). You might expect this sort of behaviour in a primitive uncivilised community, but we should know better. We should recognise that no organisation has ever been successful where there are suspicions and divisions. You cannot expect the world to have confidence in Britain if we do not have confidence in each other.

Exporting is a co-operative undertaking which involves every group and interest in the land, and we can only begin to succeed and survive as a nation if we trust each other and if we all set out to work together for those activities and undertakings which benefit the whole community and which alone can assure our future prosperity.

From the Address to the Association for
Science Education, London, November 3, 1967

FOUR

People and Buildings

IT SEEMS to me that the relationship between people and buildings falls into two categories. First, there are those factors in the built environment which exert a significant influence on the social and practical behaviour of their human communities; and, second, there are those social and practical factors of the day which determine the way in which new buildings are designed and constructed. For example, the total design concept of a cathedral or temple is obviously intended to make a particular impression upon those who use it. Equally, I think it would be fair to say that it is the attitude of the day to religious faith which is the most significant influence on the design of its temples or churches. The way they are built reflects the spirit of their age.

In the same way, the shape and design of our towns and villages reflect the course of our social evolution and, once laid out and built, they, in turn, help to determine our tastes and attitudes. Each generation builds for the needs and standards of its own day, but over-concentration on functional planning is liable to obscure one of the most important social factors in building design; what might be termed the physiology of a community. Communities are basically organic systems with a continuing and evolving existence. This means that no plan can hope for long-term success unless it takes into account the changing and evolutionary nature of the community. There can be little doubt that the integrated structure of our traditional market towns makes for a more satisfactory environment for communities than most of the planned and segregated modern developments. Of course, the pattern of evolution is not always rational or predictable. At the moment, we have the remarkable situation where the people of the so-called under-developed countries are rushing into the cities and citizens in the over-developed countries are rushing out of them; but hanging over them both are the daunting problems of sheer size, the dreaded condition called megalopolis.

Like any other organism, communities are liable to various forms of damage and disease. The symptoms of community diseases appear in their individual human members and they include such things as drunkenness, vandalism, school rowdyism, industrial militancy, corruption, general racketeering and social tensions of all kinds. There are many familiar situations at home and abroad which demonstrate only too obviously what can happen when a group of people suffers from this form of community disease.

It is really hardly necessary to add that the ordinary physical health of individual members of a community is very directly affected by the built environment. The basic rules of public health have been understood for a long time, but I am not sure that we fully appreciate the nature and extent of the influence of a particular built environment on the long term psychological health of the people born and brought up in it. I suspect that we are inclined to assume rather too easily that the health of a community depends absolutely on its wealth, its physical standards and the opportunities for its members. For every case where this may be true there is another to prove that a so-called deprived community can enjoy a vigorous spiritual and psychological health.

I sometimes feel that we need a new profession of general practitioners for community health: a sort of community engineer, capable of diagnosing the causes and prescribing the appropriate cures for troubled communities. Unfortunately, it is very difficult to quantify a satisfactory family or community. All one can do is to take certain undesirable characteristics such as disease and crime, or positive factors such as evidence of spontaneous culture and recreation, and to make statistical comparisons in relation to their built environments. So far so good, but the difficulty begins when you try to explain why there should be a difference between one family or community and another. One of the most misleading and dangerous aspects of so many reports and surveys is the uncritical assumption that a correlation exists between certain observed factors. Another is a blind faith in some academic theory unsupported by hard evidence.

I remember seeing a report in which a map of Europe showing the areas where the blood group 'O' predominated, was superimposed on a similar map showing the people's ability to pronounce 'th'. Just because the two sets of areas showed a rough coincidence this was considered sufficient to establish a correlation.

Again, it frequently seems to be assumed that all families spend exactly the same proportion of their income on housing and that everyone in a given income group wants to live together. All that can be said for certain is that the statistics for crime or culture in some communities are substantially different from others. The question is to what extent can these discrepancies be explained by the physical structure of the home or community. The trouble is that a correlation which may be true for one community is not necessarily true about another.

Oscar Newman makes this very clear in his illuminating book *Defensible Space* about public housing developments in New York. For instance, he finds a direct correlation between the height of an apartment block and the crime rate, provided that the inhabitants are of a particular social mix. On the other hand, he finds that the same type of inhabitants housed in different conditions will have much lower crime statistics. He also finds that some communities of a particular kind can exist very happily in high rise apartments. Indeed, Hong Kong would have collapsed years ago if this had not been the case. An interesting point is that, once a community settles down over several generations to a particular way of life and a particular crime rate, this will not necessarily be changed simply by moving the community into new, but otherwise similar, accommodation. There are some very obvious examples of this in some of the earlier rehousing projects in Glasgow.

Physical design can affect crime rates, but it can also affect a number of other things. It can establish or restrict easy communication and contact between neighbours and between different economic levels in society. The physical relationship between homes and places of work and between homes and the whole social infra-structure of schools, shops, hospitals, libraries, theatres and recreation facilities can establish, if not impose, a complete pattern of community existence. Added to this are the necessary provisions for modern forms of transport. Motorways and railway lines can carve up communities and create more impenetrable barriers than the Iron Curtain. One of the unfortunate consequences of industrialisation has been the development of housing areas for a very large number of people, all of whom are in similar employment at similar income levels. The absence of a mix of occupations and incomes does not help the social and cultural development of such a community. What looks neat and rational on a plan can well turn out to be a social straitjacket. On the other hand, some apparently untidy and irrational structure which has developed of its own accord may well be housing an extremely vigorous community.

I think it would be reasonable to suggest that opportunities for cultural development depend as much on the physical structure of the built environment as on the provision of cultural facilities.

But home and community life is only half the story. Most people spend the biggest proportion of their waking lives at work. We hear a lot these days about job-enrichment and there are obvious efforts to improve working conditions. But here again there is evidence that assumptions are being made which may seem rational in themselves, but which make no sort of sense when applied to particular cases.

In my experience, the conditions which create a happy atmosphere in a workshop or an office are far more complicated than such sweeping generalisations as the amount of light or the cleanliness, or the orderly arrangement of desks or machines. It is not the drawing-board which needs to be satisfied, it is the quirks and peculiarities of human nature, and there are as many regional and occupational quirks as there are occupations and regional dialects. In spite of trends towards equality between men and women, they continue to have different attitudes to work situations.

People are certainly adaptable, and if needs must they will accept a great deal; but, just as if you try to squeeze a broad foot into a narrow shoe, it is a painful business and, once a community or a work force has developed corns, it is almost impossible to cure the condition.

Of course, there are certain industrial and commercial operations which must dictate the general arrangements of the place of work, but even so there is a very great deal which can be done to adapt and reconcile the functional requirements to human idiosyncrasies. To achieve this, the development team must understand the prejudices and peculiarities of the people who are going to make the whole thing go, and it has to interpret them into the physical structure and lay-out. There are altogether too many examples of what happens if purely economic and functional requirements are allowed to dictate the features of the place of work. The economic and social arguments for monster hospitals and monster schools may be very powerful, but we do not yet know whether these particular shoes are going to pinch or whether they are going to be a comfortable fit for the individuals or the families or the communities which use them.

One of the most important features in the quality of any community is evidence of its cultural activity. The culture of a nation embraces its whole way of life, including all work and leisure activities, but the word can also be used in a more limited sense to describe the religious, aesthetic and recreational activities of a community. A Working Men's Club is as much a part of a culture as the National Theatre. The question is: how does it come about that some communities seem to have stimulated a much higher degree of cultural activity than others? What is it in a community which produces painters and poets, sculptors and musicians, playwrights and architects, choirs and dancers? Is it simply a question of providing the specialist buildings? There seems to be a general agreement that this sort of culture is a good thing, so much so that Governments spend vast sums of the taxpayers' money on culture for the people in the form of grants to theatres, orchestras, galleries and for the subsidy of artists. All these things are obviously desirable, but is this the best or the only way to encourage the development of a lively community culture? Surely the only true culture is what the people do and support spontaneously, however unclassical, and not what some well-meaning department thinks is good for them. The place for cultural instruction is in the schools and universities.

It may be sad to witness a loss of public interest in the products of what is considered to be a high standard of civilisation, but if all this talk of a changing world means anything, it means a change in cultural tastes and interests. This is a very serious dilemma for traditionalists but it needs to be recognised as a fact of life.

In this sense, I think it would be true to say that, while the modern urban industrial built environment is developing a culture of its own, it has not been responsible for any conspicuously creative cultural activity in the classic tradition. There are, of course, some notable exceptions, but the practical materialism of the industrial process seems to have inhibited that part of Man's nature which seeks to be creative and which appreciates individual creativity. Furthermore, the very considerable redistribution of wealth which has followed the process of industrialisation has removed the cultural leadership from those groups who used to exercise it.

Our problem is that we are stuck with the industrial process. Mass production has reduced the costs and, therefore, spread the goodies of technology right through society. We cannot possibly contemplate returning to some romantic notion of a more natural existence. What we can certainly do – and the sooner we get around to it the better – is to put a little more humanity into industrialism. For the moment, many believe that this can be achieved by greater participation in decision-making within industry, but industrial employment is only one factor in modern life. I suspect that greater individual responsibility in all branches of human existence must also play a part. We know enough about mankind's abiding attachment to personal freedom and independence. We know perfectly well that people have a pride and satisfaction in using their talents so as to provide for their children, their health, their leisure and their old age. The urge to create is as strong as ever and there is more than enough evidence that if we get the ground rules right the human spirit can flourish and produce remarkable achievements, even in an industrialised situation. It seems to me that there is quite an important decision to be made: do we want the human spirit of talented individuals to flourish or is it more important to insist on an absolutely fair level of existence for all? Perhaps a compromise is what we have always been looking for.

It would be ridiculous to claim that the level of cultural activity is dictated entirely by the quality of the built environment. However, I think it would be reasonable to suggest that the way in which a development team formulates its plans may have a considerable influence on the level of spontaneous cultural activity the community will ultimately achieve.

This brings me to the second aspect of our relationship with the built environment: the factors which influence the design and construction of new buildings.

The purely practical considerations such as climate, the availability of materials, technological standards, the functional purpose of the building, and so on, have always played the most important part in the design and construction of all types of buildings from mud huts to skyscrapers.

Take climate for example. This factor may not seem very important until you ignore it and put in enormous glass windows facing the sun. We are familiar enough with our own climate, where heating is necessary in winter but cooling is hardly essential in summer and proof against rain is vital all the year round. But if you forget about it, the wards end up facing north-east, while the corridors get whatever sun that area is fortunate enough to enjoy. It is true that air-conditioning and other technological gadgets can overcome climatic problems, but most of them are very expensive in energy consumption. On the whole it seems to be better to be realistic about these things and recognise the facts of nature.

Materials and techniques of construction are obviously the most important considerations because they have a direct influence on the cost.

One of the consequences of scientific research has been the development of a whole range of new materials, never previously available. When this first happened, designers and builders, uncertain how to use them properly, took a lot of trouble to make them look like traditional materials.

There was – or may still be, for all I know – a building in New York entirely clad in cast-iron plates, formed and painted to look like masonry. I shudder to think how many plastic marble columns decorate modern hotels. This phase was followed by an almost equally unhappy return to a functional honesty which merely demonstrated that, while the new materials had many practical advantages, used in an inappropriate way, most of them had no aesthetic qualities whatever of their own.

The combination of new materials and new techniques has removed virtually all restrictions on the size and shape of buildings of all kinds. The only limiting considerations left are the cost and the system by which the project is financed. But considerations of cost and systems of finance can operate both ways. It can – at least in theory – limit the maximum size of a project but, perhaps more important, it can also put a limit on the minimum size of a development if not on an individual building. This economic factor, sometimes called the economy of scale, favours gigantism and it has proportionately a greater influence on all types of building today than at any time in history.

The combination of economic and technological factors is inclined to encourage standardisation at the lowest common denominator. The modern industrialised system requires a large proportion of the population to be employed in factories. This in turn has led to the row upon row of identical housing which is such a feature of our major industrial cities. Just as technical and design standards make it possible to improve this situation, so rising costs are dictating that housing developments have to be on a larger scale than ever, and the effect of any mistakes is therefore greater than ever.

It has been amply and frequently proved how disastrous it is to design to some generalised formula about density and open space. The classic example must be the award-winning housing development at Pruitt-Igo in St Louis which had to be demolished within ten years of construction as its community gradually degenerated into criminal anarchy. Standards of density and open space have to be related to human requirements and usefulness.

Still very much among the practical factors are the legal and planning constraints. I daresay there are, or were, good reasons for each bit of this mass of complicated legislation, but they are not always obvious at first sight. As so often happens with written regulations, even when the reasons for them do become clear, their effect seldom turns out to be exactly what was intended.

All these practical factors affecting the design and construction of buildings have to be put together and reconciled with the purpose of the building and the requirements of the owner or developer. This is where we leave the firm ground of fact and step into the world of taste and value – judgements, social and political attitudes and intellectual background. In spite of all the apparently overwhelming influence of the practical factors, the ultimate design still depends on the intellectual qualities of architects and their clients and the technical skills of builders. It is out of this meld of attitude and temperament that buildings of distinction or monstrosity, of soaring inspiration or depressing vulgarity, are created or perpetuated as the case may be.

This is not just a matter of technical competence or even of a social conscience. The fact is that the end product is a reflection of both the individual mentality and philosophy of architect and client, including – as I have already suggested – a reflection of the group attitudes of the community and period in which they grew up, live and work. No amount of self-conscious attempts to follow a style or fashion can make up for lack of talent or inspiration. The jargon of radiant cities, high-rise, glass skins, and separation of human activities, may satisfy the intellect, but it is just as likely to create cultural deserts. Uncritical acceptance of social or political housing policies which ignore the realities of human nature can demoralise a community in a very short time. If the heart and mind are not totally committed to the work of achieving a sensible and humane solution, the result is no better than a sham; and, furthermore, the sham is itself indicative of the state of the society which tolerates it.

All designers and developers have a choice to make. They can either design with an eye to the reaction of their colleagues, or to avoid an expected line of criticism: a fairly safe but entirely negative approach; or they can decide to trust their own talent and judgement and to acknowledge the experience of others and make their designs a positive statement of their attitude and philosophy towards their fellow citizens. This takes a great deal of courage and involves considerable risk, but it is the only chance of creating something of lasting merit.

There is often a tendency to believe that every feature of a design can be reduced to some functional formula, and if there is no apparent formula then there is bound to be a self-evident criterion. For instance, an accepted formula for the zoning of cities is the functional separation of industry, housing, commerce and shopping. It is simply assumed to be self-evident that there must be such zones; and, anyway, it makes planning easier. The fact that segregation of housing by income-group is socially divisive and often results in the lowest paid citizens having the furthest to travel to their employment, or that the majority of modern factories are neither noisy nor obnoxious, or that all the members of a family, or people in a group of houses, are not all employed in the same sort of jobs, tends to be completely ignored.

In the very simplest social system, a person wanting a house has to build it with his own labour. As far as Britain is concerned, things have become so difficult and complicated that we are actually getting back to square one. There are architects and builders, consultants and surveyors, planners, speculators and housing associations and landlords, tenants and tied houses, local housing authorities and building societies and a veritable jungle of rates, taxes and subsidies – all controlled by a mountain of legislation and a vast bureaucracy. I am inclined to doubt whether the economy of scale applies to bureaucracy. It seems more likely that the bigger the bureaucracy, the greater the waste of money and paper, and the longer it takes to reach a decision. A visitor from outer space might be forgiven for being a bit surprised at this system, but if one went on to explain that it was really intended to make things easier and to achieve greater social justice, I do not think he would need much encouragement to return home by the quickest route.

Much as we might like to be able to start all over again from scratch, we are stuck with a vast legacy of structures and systems reaching back well over a thousand years. Even the most radical revolution cannot erase this inheritance. And, even if it could be done, we would merely be laying the foundation for another period of evolution. We have got to live with our inheritance. No generation can hope to create instant Utopia – the best we can do is to cherish the best of our inheritance while recognising the most unsatisfactory features and trying to put them right; to adapt, and improve, what we have, and to do our share of intelligent innovation for the next generation to criticise and rearrange in its time.

Unfortunately, every indication suggests that the building industry is in a bad way at the present time. Industrial and commercial construction is not exactly buoyant. Whereas in 1972 something like 350,000 new houses were started, this figure dropped to 250,000 in 1974, while the average time to complete a public sector house went up from 16 months in 1969 to 21.3 months in 1974. At a time when about one in five of our total of 19 million houses is said to be more or less inadequate, the number of houses improved dropped from about 450,000 in 1973 to about 300,000 in 1974. All this has happened in spite of the fact that Government expenditure on housing has gone up from 2 to 5½ per cent of its total revenue in the last ten years. Just to make matters worse, the supply of accommodation to let has almost completely dried up. Some people might feel like adding to this tale of woe by maintaining that hardly any buildings of aesthetic merit have been constructed in recent years, and that the fruits of planning, which were forecast with such confidence about twenty years ago, have not been quite so succulent as we were led to expect.

One of the most disappointing features of the present situation is that hundreds of small building firms, representing a wealth of independent initiative and responsible for a very large proportion of the house maintenace and repair work, are being forced out of business or being threatened with extinction. I refuse to believe that everyone wants to live largely at the expense of the rapidly-dwindling proportion of the rest of the community, but unless the small builders survive, thousands of people who want to build and own their homes will never be able to achieve this fundamental human right, and a very large proportion of existing home-owners will be unable to find anyone to do the essential maintenance and repairs.

Far be it from me to attempt to diagnose the disease, but I can only say that I would not be in the least surprised if someone was able to show that the number of houses started or improved declined in direct proportion to the volume of housing legislation or to the increase in the number of administrators employed. This is no reflection on the individual competence of the administrators. It is simply sheer numbers that seem to inhibit rapid and effective action.

Of course, the picture is not one of unrelieved gloom. Many local authorities have done surprisingly well. Housing Associations and Trusts have had generous help and achieved a great deal with it. More recently, the Housing Corporation has appeared on the scene and looks like making a considerable impression. Perhaps a more significant development has been the appearance of a sizeable group of do-it-yourself house-builders. They deserve full marks for initiative, but it is a sad reflection on the state of affairs that a highly-developed and -organised society such as ours has been forced back into this most primitive system of acquiring a home.

An encouraging sign is the amount of money going into Building Societies. This is extremely important because our whole system depends on the reinvestment of savings into new capital works, particularly into housing and the wealth creating industries. There is something desperately wrong if people find it better to put their savings into totally sterile and non-productive works of art as a form of investment. The money for all investment comes from savings. It is no good bleating about low levels of investment in housing and industry if there is no positive encouragement to save.

Things have obviously not always been quite as bad as this, so one might well be forgiven for wondering what has gone wrong. The need for houses, offices, factories and public buildings of all sorts is greater than ever. The building industry is willing, anxious and technically capable of providing them, and, in spite of the present economic situation, there is every reason to believe that adequate finance is available.

Of one thing I am entirely convinced: the existing situation is demonstrably not the fault of builders. You have only to look around you to see what good builders have been able to do in the past and there is no shred of evidence to suggest that they could not be doing as well, if not better, at this moment. No one can suggest that the skill of craftsmen, the ability of managers and the capacity to finance has simply collapsed in a heap of rubble. Somehow or other, we seem to have got ourselves into the clutches of a legislative and administrative structure which effectively prevents these obvious abilities of a willing industry from meeting our obvious needs.

I see no reason why we should not aim to get the best from the industrial process as well as the most satisfactory human society, based, not on some idealised view of the way humanity should be, but on a rational and objective understanding of human nature as it is and as it has been for a very long time.

*From a Lecture to the Institute of Building,
London, May 20, 1975*

FIVE

In Praise of Engineering

ABOUT THE only certainty in human affairs is that they are never in a steady state. The pendulum of popular attitude is always swinging one way or the other. From the Industrial Revolution until about the end of the First World War the pendulum swung in favour of engineers, and the period of our greatest national prosperity coincided with our greatest engineering enterprise. Since then things have not been quite so easy.

The trouble with success is that it takes a long time before its unpleasant consequences become known. Engineering was inevitably linked with the industrialisation of this country which, although it led the world in the output of manufactured goods and wealth creation, was also responsible for the appalling human conditions in the great and growing industrial cities; and, in addition, the period after the First War saw the growth of anti-capitalist attitudes, which were given considerable encouragement, first by the German hyper-inflation and then by the American depression. And, not unexpectedly, capitalism was seen to include industrialism.

The trouble with the pendulum is that it does not discriminate between good and bad; once it swings it takes everything with it. The swing against the system, which allowed vast profits to be made while so many lived in squalor, was quite indiscriminate, and everything which appeared to be associated with capitalism and industrialism became a target for attack. It is really only a few years ago, and to a certain extent even now, that a career in industry or commerce was denounced as joining a rat race. Whole volumes of controlling legislation are still being added to the statute book, doubtless for the best possible reasons, but not always with the expected consequences. Little wonder then that people already involved become somewhat discouraged and demoralised, and many who might have become engineers are put off.

Other things happened as well. The last war gave a tremendous stimulus to invention. There was a neeed for every sort of offensive and defensive gadget, and anyone who could turn scientific knowledge into some useful military service was highly regarded. Unfortunately in the popular view all this work was scientific and the work of scientists.

Now, I have nothing against scientists, indeed I have a tremendous admiration for them, but the work of inventing and producing these military gadgets, even though scientists may have been involved, was engineering. The consequence of this misconception, I believe, was that science got all the credit for these devices – while engineering became synonymous with production and maintenance. It may well be that this was one of the reasons for science becoming more popular in schools and the scientific research programme after the war reaching almost astronomical proportions.

There was a further factor in the swing against engineering. Soon after the Second War people began to recognise that irresponsible development was beginning to have quite significant effects on the natural environment. The most obvious was, I suppose, industrial pollution – and those in the country noticed it most with the use of toxic chemicals in agriculture – but it did not take long for every kind of industrial development to come under attack for spoiling the environment. Once again the engineer found himself on the defensive. The irony is that the only people who can develop and install the equipment for controlling pollution are engineers.

I hardly dare suggest that the pendulum is beginning to swing the other way, but at least there is evidence that it is getting near the end of its travel. The fact is that extremes of industrial revolution have been or are still being corrected, but we live in a mechanical age and we cannot hope to maintain, let alone improve, our own conditions or the conditions in the less developed countries if the people chiefly responsible for the present state and future development of technology are treated as second-class citizens.

As a country with hardly any natural resources to speak of – and I think it would be very unwise to assume that North Sea gas and oil can get us out of our difficulties without any further effort on our part – we depend, more than any other nation, on our ability to convert imported raw materials into goods we can sell overseas, and on the services we can offer to foreign customers. With a population of some 55 million living at a fairly high density on a small island I think we are doing pretty well to produce some 60 per cent of our food requirements; and that after all is a major engineering activity. But in the long run we have got to live by our commercial and industrial wits; and in industry the most important wits are the engineers. So I must confess it is a total mystery to me that engineering is not the most encouraged, popular, prosperous and respected profession in the country. In my opinion, if we had our priorities right, it would be just that.

It seems to be dawning on us, rather slowly perhaps, that a swing too far against engineering creates as many problems as the excessive swing towards engineering produced a hundred years ago. However, if there is to be a swing back, it does not mean that the pendulum will return to where it was before. Time has carried the whole organisation forward and during that span a great deal has happened.

For one thing the majority of the engineers of the last century had little or no formal training, so that their successes depended almost entirely on imagination and ingenuity, together with guesswork modified by trial and error, and always of course on tremendous determination. In spite of that, their achievements were really spectacular. In fact we still do not really give them credit for what they did with the limited scientific knowledge and even more limited materials available to them.

For instance I do not think we appreciate that the graceful corn-grinding windmills of 200 years ago incorporated variable pitch, automatic constant speed controls by varying the pressure between the millstones, rotor-brakes, overspeed and underspeed warning systems, collective pitch change mechanisms and various other devices which aeronautical engineers are probably convinced are all quite modern. Paxton's Crystal Palace is better remembered for the fire which destroyed it rather than for the introduction of modular prefabrication for large scale buildings.

There is obviously a lot of that kind of empirical engineering going on today, but if you look at the problems of space and supersonic flight, nuclear power, broadcasting and television and the whole range of man-made fibres and materials, it is quite obvious that these could only be achieved by highly-trained specialists. These are the real professional engineers of today and they are occupied in the whole range of engineering activities: invention and exploitation of scientific knowledge, design, development, production and maintenance. Life as we know it today could not go on without them, and the better they are as engineers the better will life go on.

We know from history that very many people in this country have talents to be engineers. I suspect this is due partly to the effects of the pendulum and partly to the relatively less attractive prospects of a career in engineering. I believe we shall be able to say that the pendulum is beginning to swing back when the career prospects in engineering begin to improve.

In the meanwhile anyone with the will and the talent for engineering has to begin by meeting the challenge of the training process. There, the prospective engineer will find himself involved in the permanent state of conflict between what the academics want to teach and what all sorts of employers and self-appointed experts think he needs to know. There is nothing wrong with this conflict until some well-meaning people start to talk about the needs of the nation as if the training of engineers could be equated with a manufacturing process whose end products ought to be useful to the state. This is just the attitude which really would transform a socially valuable profession into a rat race.

This is the doctrine of Orwell's *1984*, and that is not far away. In a free society composed of intelligent and responsible people the whole purpose of education and training is to allow each individual to develop his talents and gifts so that he can put them to the best possible use for himself, his family, his community and his fellow men in general.

No matter what sort of world the theorists like to see, it should be self-evident to most people that talents of skill and intelligence are not evenly distributed among mankind. It may be unfair but some people are better at mathematics, some are more ambitious, others can develop great skill with their hands. There are places for all these capacities in engineering, and the Engineering Industry Training Board, the City and Guilds of London Institute, the Technician Education Council and the Council of Engineering Institutions each provide the means for people to qualify in their appropriate category. The relevant courses are available at technical colleges, polytechnics and universities.

This is all very admirable, but the vital factor is that all these qualifications should be related to one another in such a way that each qualification is taken into consideration in the training course for the next one. It should always be possible for someone starting as an operative, or anywhere on the ladder, to see a series of ladders leading to higher qualifications right through to chartered engineer; because freedom to exploit one's talents is just as important as freedom of speech.

As the whole business of engineering has become more sophisticated so the resources necessary to train engineers have become more elaborate and, equally important, the number of highly qualified and intelligent engineers required for teaching has greatly increased. This teaching function is vital, but the quality of the teaching is vastly improved if the teachers are allowed to participate in the real industrial engineering world. A number of universities have set up special research and development departments run on commercial lines with the object of offering the facilities of the university, and the talent of the staff and students, to industrial customers. This is interesting work for staff and students alike and it has the added value that, while it makes them aware of the commercial facts of life, it also gives their customers a better appreciation of the competence of academic staff and students.

The next hurdle comes between learning and doing. It is trite to say that knowledge of theory and principle is not sufficient qualification for responsible practice in engineering. It may be enough for economists, priests and politicians but for the engineer there is an extra requirement for experience and understanding of the practical issues of his chosen specialisation. The politician and the priest never fail to escape the consequences of their mistakes, but mistakes made by engineers are there for all to see, explanations and excuses notwithstanding.

There are basically two ways of getting over this problem of converting from learning to doing. It is either by a straight-through course and qualifying examination followed by a period of indoctrination training, or it can be achieved by some sort of sandwich system consisting of periods of practical experience. Both these systems have their advantages and disadvantages, but in my experience it is much easier to learn and to appreciate the instruction if it is given against the background of some practical experience. For instance in my case I found it much easier to follow the technical details of ship construction after a spell at sea.

The student, now hopefully still retaining his enthusiasm and his talents, eventually joins the ranks of professional engineers and finds himself confronted by the professional institutions and the C.E.I. I suspect that many engineers fail to see the importance of the professional institutions. They want to get on with their work and they do not want to be bothered by anything else. However they fail to see that democracy is not simply a case of elected assemblies for political discussion and decision.

Democracy, amongst other things, means self-government and the professional institutions are the means by which engineers, and indeed all other professions, govern their own affairs and ensure that the public can rely on the services offered by professional engineers. I suppose this function could be performed by state-employed officials, but it would mean yet one more loss of freedom and responsibility by private citizens.

The choice of specialisation by engineers is already very wide and is constantly getting wider. At the same time engineering projects have become so complicated that they can only succeed through the co-operation of the whole spectrum of specialists. This grouping of several specialisations for a particular function such as aviation, transport, communication, construction, underwater engineering and power, has brought into existence a whole new range of inter-disciplinary bodies which I am sure will have an increasingly important part to play in the future.

In spite of all this diversification there will always be a group of people which is covered by the general description of engineer and it forms a very important sector in our national life. The common interests of all engineers, that is of all specialisations, have of course been recognised for some time but it is only recently that the C.E.I. has established the Fellowship of Engineering. Drawing its membership from across the board of the engineering specialisations and selecting the most successful and accomplished engineers, it has taken on the task of looking after the general interests of engineers and engineering as a whole within the larger framework of our national life.

Whatever specialisation an engineer may choose, he also has the further choice of what function he wishes to perform. He can take to design, for instance, which is really the beginning of all projects. Apart from a need for imagination and inventiveness the designer has to be in closest touch with the world outside engineering. Social needs, economic trends and possibilities, popular attitudes, materials and scientific discoveries have all got to influence his designs.

In fact, he acts as the interpreter between the dreams and ambitions of people and their realisation. Whatever those economists, priests and politicians may say, the ultimate architect of the whole human environment is the engineer as designer. In that sense he has a much greater influence on social conditions than popular fancy has ever imagined. It is high time that this is recognised particularly by engineers themselves as well as by people responsible for their education and training.

An engineer can also choose to be a manager and, contrary to popular political belief, management skills are seldom very effective without a sound technical understanding of the project being managed. The engineer as a manager knows what the job is about, and provided he has the talent for management he is in a far better position to see that it is done properly. There is a lot of wisdom in the old Service precept that you should never ask anyone to do something which you cannot do yourself.

Neither designers nor managers would have much to do unless someone started a project. The usual term for this sort of person is an entrepreneur, a French word. The literal translation into English is undertaker, which is doubtless the reason we use the French word. But the fact remains that, again contrary to popular belief, employment can only be created by employers, by people prepared to undertake to do something, to take the responsibility for starting an enterprise.

The engineer has exceptional opportunities to become an employer, but like all other choices it does require rather special talents. Unfortunately it is not as popular as it ought to be because, while the risks of failure are as great as ever, the advantages of success in these days are not quite as apparent as they ought to be.

One of the remarkable features of our national life is the extraordinary way in which people seem to be persuaded by slogans and parrot cries. We have just come through a period when the slogan was 'Bigger is inevitably better'. It is of course perfectly true that long runs of mass-produced goods are cheaper, but anyone who dared to suggest that people might not work as hard or as willingly for the big organisations as they did for the small were simply ignored. Neither did the enthusiasts appear to consider the possibility of a big organisation getting into trouble. If the advantages of success appeared to be greater it should perhaps not have escaped notice that the consequences of failure were likely to be disastrous.

Least of all did anyone seem to realise that, while there are lots of people capable of managing relatively small organisations extremely well, it is much less certain that the necessary exceptional talent can always be found to give the same standard of management to the very big organisations.

The great cry is that we are going to be saved by investment. To begin with it is a term which we use in two different senses, and this causes endless confusion. In one sense it describes the use of that proportion of the profits retained by a company to buy and install new plant and machinery. In the other sense it describes the use of savings by individuals to buy shares and bonds, or the use of income by pension and insurance institutions to do the same thing in order to earn dividends; or, if the dividends yield is made unattractive by taxation or some other reason, then the investment is made in the hope of capital appreciation.

Of course the danger of making capital appreciation more attractive than dividends is that only productive enterprises can yield dividends, but all sorts of useless objects like pictures, jewels, whisky or Krugerrands can appreciate in capital value.

The only similarity between the two kinds of investment is the hope of a return on the money invested. Investment, no matter where it comes from, if it produces no return is money wasted. Therefore investment as such is certainly not going to improve our industrial and manufacturing performance. All investment can do is to make it possible to achieve higher productivity and greater output, and it can stimulate new enterprises; but in neither kind of investment can it guarantee success.

Perhaps the most important function of investment of either kind is to provide risk capital, which means capital to start something new, or, in other words innovation. This sort of investment will only be available if the chances of success are reasonably balanced against the risks of failure, but if the chances of success are too severely hindered for any reason, it will no longer be forthcoming, and that means that there will be a lot of frustrated engineers unable and unwilling to exploit their ideas and inventions. And it will also, I think, discourage them from setting out on their own to become creators of employment. And, furthermore, new enterprises are vitally needed to balance the loss of employment in companies and industries which are no longer viable for whatever reason.

One of the most under-rated, and until recently almost totally neglected, choices of specialisation for an engineer comes in the broad category of maintenance. It is true that very large numbers of engineers have found themselves spending a great deal of their time on maintenance of plant and machinery, but it is only slowly beginning to become apparent that this work requires its own particular talents and attitudes. No matter how well the designer and builder have done their jobs it still rests with the maintenance to get the best out of what they have produced. Furthermore, of course, the experience of maintenance engineers has a vital importance to designers and makers.

For example a helicopter which only requires two hours' maintenance for every hour it flies is a viable proposition. If it requires ten hours' maintenance for every hour in the air, regardless of how impressive its operational performance, it is still going to be a disaster. Concorde does everything its makers said it would, but its success in airline service is going to depend on its maintainability and freedom from snags.

We give great credit to the engineers who design and construct the dams and power stations, the reservoirs and the water works, the railways and the airliners, the roads and the sewage treatment plants, but we tend to forget that someone has got to keep them all working efficiently and, more often than not, for a good deal longer than originally intended. The same is true in industry. If the plant does not function the operators cannot produce.

Every engineer is also a person and a citizen. As likely as not he is a husband, father and house-owner, and there is no reason why he should not be a sportsman, politician and artist as well. We have got so used to putting people into categories that we are inclined to forget that all individuals belong to a whole series of categories, and make their contributions to the community in a number of different ways. The only qualities which an individual takes with him into each category to which he belongs are his common sense and intelligence, his character and his judgement. As a successful engineer requires these qualities in fairly full measure, it stands to reason that he should have a particularly valuable influence within the other categories to which he belongs.

After all, the life of a community is not governed entirely by custom and legislation. These things can make it more or less difficult, but what really establishes the state of a community is the morality and standards, the attitude and ambitions, of the individuals who compose it. People who happen to be engineers carry the same responsibility for these standards as anyone else, if not a greater one.

If there is a danger of putting people into categories there is an even greater danger of confusing abstract concepts with real life. We talk about 'industry', 'the national economy' and the 'arts' as if they each had an existence of their own. In fact, of course, industry is not what matters at all. It is the people involved in industrial enterprises we should be concerned about. The national economy is a figment created by statisticians; in practice the national economy is no more than a reflection of the circumstances of individual citizens. The economy is only prosperous if the people and their enterprises are prosperous. The same applies to the arts. They cannot be spread on to popular culture by act of legislation. To be a true expression of popular taste they must be the product of the direct interaction between artists and their customers.

If we take away the categories and the generalisations, in the end we come down to personal ambitions and the personal motivations of the individual. These are part of his human nature, and I doubt whether even the most vigorous brainwashing and political indoctrination will do more than dull the edges of his human nature. People will always want to succeed in the eyes of their fellow men. I suspect they will always want to have, for instance, a home they can genuinely call their own. I believe they will always want to do the best they can for their children. Furthermore, it seems wholly natural that they should wish those of their children who are properly qualified to carry on a successful family enterprise. And I also suspect that it gives people with a sense of responsibility a real feeling of achievement to be able to provide for the health care of their families, and to make them independent in their old age, if they possibly can.

I may be a bit old-fashioned to suggest this, but I have little doubt that most reasonable people like to feel that they personally are making some useful contribution to the success of their countries. I daresay that there are many other motivations, but it seems to me that anything which gives people the opportunity to achieve these ambitions is an incentive, but if it happens to be legal, morally sound and not too fattening – like engineering for instance – then so much the better.

From an Address to the Birmingham and West Midlands Region of the Engineering Industries' Association, November 16, 1976

SIX

The Present State of Industrialism

I DO not think it would be reasonable to suggest that anyone planned or plotted the Industrial Revolution, and hence all the problems of today's urban/industrial society in which most of the world seems to be living – or to which they are rapidly advancing. It was people left to their own devices who decided, in such large numbers, that city life – even in slums – and industrial employment were preferable to primitive country life and agricultural hard labour.

We have now inherited the problems which that revolution created, but added to them are the consequences of a great deal of well-intentioned legislation designed to solve them. All sorts of theories and practices have been tried in an effort to cope with this new phenomenon of the concentrated urban industrial society. Capitalism, Communism, Nationalism, Socialism, profit-sharing, participation and the Corporate State have all offered solutions, but none of them seems to have the complete answer to what might be described as our present state of industrialism.

By that I mean the evolution of a whole new pattern of work and a whole new structure of human relationships, which naturally have come to be known as industrial relations. All the parables in the Bible relate to agriculture. Today, the industrial experience, rather than the agricultural experience, has come to be the common denominator, and to such an extent that industrial criteria have influenced every other part of human experience. Horse-racing and -breeding have become the bloodstock industry. Music and drama, together with television and films, are now part of the entertainment industry.

The churches are said to be marketing a product. Any group of people which withdraws its contribution to the needs of society, be they nurses or coalminers, are said to be taking industrial action. Defence equipment has to be cost-effective and education has become a process for investing in the human resource and for producing an article to meet the needs of industry. Even students have been known to refuse to work in imitation of industrial workers withdrawing their labour.

Parliaments also seem to have been infected by the standards of industrialism. For instance I get the impression that legislation is looked upon as the Parliamentary product, and the success of a session is liable to be rated according to the number of new laws added to the statute book. I think there are times when we have all felt that Parliaments should go a stage further and improve their quality-control arrangements.

One of the most important features of industrialism is the evolution of communities totally orientated towards providing the industrial labour force – no longer interdependent communities where the supply and demand for a whole range of labour and services covered a wide spectrum of skill and enterprise, but where a whole community becomes dependent on a limited level and choice of employment opportunities offered by a single industry. Even if there is more than one major employer the people find themselves tenants of a single housing authority, either company-based, or an agency of the local authority.

These communities are something quite novel in human experience. The material conditions are probably better than ever before. Power, light, water, sewage and roads are provided, yet the health of the communities themselves varies very greatly. Measured in terms of the incidence of such community diseases as alcoholism, vandalism, mugging and social, racial and religious friction, there are a good many communities which can only be described as sick. But we do not really know for certain whether it is the place that makes the people or whether it is the people who make the place.

I believe we need a new kind of profession or professional agency – something like a community physician – capable of diagnosing community diseases as well as prescribing the cures. At the moment, we rely on such things as comprehensive political theories which are supposed to provide all the answers; or we let prejudice decide or simply expect an amateur enthusiasm to do good. I feel that, just because people have been elected to or promoted to positions of authority, they must automatically know better and therefore that they have a special right to decide what is good for their fellow citizens.

I believe that this attitude has led to one of the most interesting features of industrialism, and that is the importance attached to planning. Planning naturally plays a very important part in industry, in so far as it is needed to provide the infra-structure of community services, but there is a big difference between planning for things and planning for people. Just because the planning process is successful in the industrial context does not mean to say that it can be used as an infallible cure-all by social planners, by which I mean the designers of housing developments, town planners, allocators of educational resources, curriculum planners, health, recreation and welfare planners and, of course, the economic planners.

One of the dangers is that, under the institutional planners, statistics and percentages and national prestige are liable to become more important than people, and the whole system is liable to become oppressively paternalistic.

I am not suggesting that there is anything wrong with planners as people, indeed let me hasten to say that they all do their best, and with the best possible intentions, and they have undoubtedly many successes to their credit. The difficulty about planning for people is that planning is a rational operation while human nature – even in this great age of human enlightenment – remains as irrational as ever; and, as both the planners and the planned-for share this irrational human nature, the consequences of social planning are frequently as irrational as you might expect.

It is extraordinary to think that we know more about science and about our universe and our planet; about our own history and psychology; we pride ourselves on being more socially conscious, and yet we go on making the most elementary mistakes, and even quite intelligent people continue to be capable of puerile, selfish, cruel and destructive behaviour.

We talk about morality and tolerance, trust and co-operation, peace and friendship, yet every day the media provide horrifying evidence of the reverse.

It is all very confusing. The age of the social conscience, social justice and concern seems to have coincided with the age of crime, pornography, mugging, selfish indulgence and international terrorism. What started out as a liberalisation of restrictive social conventions seems to have developed into a dictatorship of licence.

I suspect that the explanation is that the world can accumulate knowledge and experience, though all that ends by being stored in libraries and computers, while every human baby is born totally ignorant. Consequently, the whole process of teaching and learning has to begin from the beginning with every child, and the more complicated the society it is born into, the more difficult the problem becomes. It is only too apparent that it is possible for communities to achieve quite high standards of material development with, at the same time, the moral and behavioural standards of a colony of monkeys.

It is not just the teaching of facts – indeed they are really only useful in an academic or occupational sense – what is much more important is attitudes, behavioural standards, emotions and prejudices. Great academics and engineers are given credit for their special talents but, in the community at large, people are judged by their behaviour, by their relationship to other people, and by their influence on other people.

I suspect that what industrialism has done for mankind is to give it the impression that everything in the world from children's play to a housing estate can be planned and made to function with the efficiency of a nuclear power station. Whereas the real truth is that, whatever our material achievements, we are still human, and that it is the facts of human nature and not the binary system which must govern human affairs.

From an Address to the Canadian Club,
October 17, 1977